SOVIET
AIR POWER

SOVIET
AIR POWER

ANTHONY ROBINSON

Bison Books

First published in 1985 by
Bison Books Ltd
176 Old Brompton Road
London SW5
England

ISBN 0 86124 180 0

Printed in Hong Kong

PREVIOUS PAGES: A
Mikoyan MiG-23
Flogger-G air defense
fighter of the Soviet Air
Force. The variable-
geometry Flogger has
proved an able successor
to the MiG-21 from the
same design bureau.
THIS PAGE: Ilyushin's
mighty Il-76 turbofan
transport prepares for
the imminent
embarkation of up to
120 paratroopers.

CONTENTS

1 THE SOVIET WAY IN WARFARE   Page 6

2 THE ORGANIZATION OF AIR POWER   24

3 STRATEGIC MISSILE AND ROCKET FORCES   46

4 AIR DEFENSE AND SPACE FORCES   68

5 TACTICAL AIR POWER   88

6 BATTLEFIELD HELICOPTER FORCES   100

7 AIR TRANSPORT AND TRAINING   118

8 NAVAL AVIATION   138

9 SOVIET AIR POWER IN ACTION   162

CHAPTER ONE
THE SOVIET WAY IN WARFARE

Soviet views of air power differ from generally-accepted Western concepts in many ways. For example, even at such a fundamental level as the organization of military forces there are striking dissimilarities. Whereas most Western forces are organized into army, navy and air force, in the Soviet Union, in addition to these three services, there are the Air Defense Forces and Strategic Rocket Forces, both of which exist as entirely separate services. Furthermore, whereas Western practice is usually to assign battlefield support helicopters to an army air arm and naval aviation units to a naval air force, in the Soviet Union both these elements are part of the air force organization. Soviet thinking on warfare is idiosyncratic and it is necessary to examine how a distinctive Soviet military doctrine shapes the organization, equipment and employment of air forces.

Many factors have combined to produce a Soviet way in warfare. They include the Soviet historical experience, developments in military technology and aspects of the Russian (as distinct from Soviet) character, environment and national consciousness. However, preeminent amongst these determinants are the requirements of Communist ideology. The Communist Party of the Soviet Union, at any rate in theory, claims to control all aspects of Soviet life. In practice its influence, while falling short of the ideal, is nonetheless immense. In the armed forces, political officers operate at all levels and are responsible for the morale of personnel, as well as for their political education. In the Soviet air force, the commander-in-chief has a political deputy of colonel-general rank, who has equivalent status to the head of engineering and technical services, for example. The armed forces are an instrument of the Communist Party in accordance with Lenin's dictum (echoing the German military philosopher Carl von Clausewitz) that war is a tool of policy.

Defense of the Revolution and the Socialist State has been a primary aim of Soviet military policy throughout the existence of the USSR. This is a responsibility not simply of the armed forces, but of the entire population. Indeed the Soviet Union is in many respects a nation in arms, with military policy affecting many aspects of Soviet life, including most notably the economy and education. Although it is by most standards highly inefficient, the Soviet economy is well geared to the needs of military production. All male Soviet children are given pre-service military instruction in school, covering such basic skills as drill and weapons handling, as part of the standard secondary education syllabus. Furthermore all Soviet citizens are constantly reminded not only of the role of the armed forces in Soviet society but also of their personal responsibilities to the defense of the State. All Soviet males are liable for military service, conscripts serving in the air force for a period of two years, and after completing their service they are liable to be recalled as reservists

PREVIOUS PAGES: A MiG-23 visits Finland, 1978. Aircraft on such 'exchange' visits with foreign countries have invariably been stripped of 'sensitive' items of combat equipment.

until they reach the age of 50. There are a number of quasi-military volunteer organizations, including the DOSAAF (*Dobrovol'noe obshchestvo sodeistviya Armii, Aviatsii i Flotu* – Voluntary Society for the Support of the Army, Aviation and Navy), and many Soviet citizens are involved in the extensive civil defense program. All these activities, together with the considerable publicity given to the armed forces in newspapers, television and radio broadcasts, serve to create an atmosphere, if not of a state under siege, at any rate of a society which must be constantly prepared to go to war in defense of its vital interests.

Soviet ideology does not simply require that the gains of the Revolution be defended, but it strongly urges the export of Revolution by military means. A basic tenet of Marxist-Leninist theory is that socialism will inevitably triumph over capitalism. Soviet theorists point to the outcome of World War II – or in Soviet terminology the Great Patriotic War – as an illustration of the irreversible character of socialist progress. In spite of the enormous casualties suffered during the war, the Soviet Union in 1945 was in a stronger position than ever before. It had exported its system of government to the states of Eastern Europe, thus creating a bloc of socialist countries on which it could depend for military and economic assistance. Furthermore it had acquired a useful buffer zone between Soviet territory and its potential enemies in Western Europe. These sub-

stantial gains were entirely due to military action. Yet, however desirable the export of revolution on the point of a bayonet was in theory, in practice Soviet postwar policy towards capitalist states (and to those socialist states which refuse to accept the Soviet Marxist-Leninist line) has been tempered by a degree of caution.

The Soviet Union is no more anxious to become involved in a major war than are the nations of the West. This is even more true of a nuclear war, as the Soviet leadership fully realizes that this would result in an unprecedented degree of destruction and represent a catastrophe from which the Soviet state would be unlikely to recover. In the event of a major war in Western Europe, the Soviet Union will attempt to achieve victory by conventional means. Paradoxically it sees its own preparedness to fight at the theater nuclear and strategic nuclear levels as an insurance against the conflict escalating. In the Soviet view, the shift in NATO defensive strategy from massive retaliation (whereby a Soviet attack in Europe would be countered by the immediate use of American strategic nuclear weapons against the Soviet homeland) to a strategy of flexible response (a conventional defense, backed by the threat of the use of tactical nuclear weapons within a few days) was forced on NATO by the development of a credible Soviet nuclear force in the 1960s. Consequently Soviet military doctrine aims to achieve a decisive conventional victory before NATO commanders can secure the release of tactical nuclear weapons from their political masters. It is typical of Soviet military attitudes that, whereas it regards its own nuclear strategy as one of restraining (in Russian *sderzhivat*) the aggressor, American deterrence is derided as *ustrasheniye* or terror.

Although the Soviet Union is anxious to avoid direct military confrontation with the United States, it is not prepared to forgo the struggle to achieve world hegemony, which it refers to as the Era of Global Democratic Peace. It sees many opportunities of pursuing this aim by 'peaceful' means. For example the Soviet Union fosters conflict in such areas of the Third World as Latin America and Africa, often supporting left-wing régimes or insurgent forces by proxy through Cuban forces. In the West a major Soviet objective is to isolate the European nations from the United States and to bring about the dissolution of the NATO alliance. Even non-military groupings such as the European Economic Community are seen as standing in the way of Soviet aims. A fragmented Western Europe could be easily intimidated by Soviet military power, without the necessity of overt military action to achieve political domination. American commentators have referred to this process as 'Finlandization,' a definition that does less than justice to Finland's remarkable efforts to avoid becoming the sixteenth Soviet Socialist Republic. Nonetheless, no less an authority than former Party Secretary Yuri Andropov has held up Finnish-Soviet relations as 'the very kind of détente which makes for a more lasting peace.' Détente in Soviet eyes is simply a continuation of the inevitable struggle between communism and capitalism by means other than war. The Soviet Union aims to dominate rivals and will not accept the status quo on any other terms.

If Communist ideology has played the major role in shaping Soviet strategy, purely Russian concerns have also left their imprint on the Soviet military mind. One illustration of this influence is the

LEFT: A Mil Mi-8 twin-turbine helicopter of Finland's Ilmavoimat undergoes maintenance. Finland has been the recipient of much Soviet equipment in past years.

primacy of land warfare in Soviet military doctrine. The Soviet armed forces are tailored to operations over the vast expanse of Soviet territory, which has been the battleground of Soviet and Imperial Russian armies for centuries. Sea power, the much publicized naval expansion under Admiral Sergei Gorshkov in the 1960s and 1970s notwithstanding, has always been a peripheral Russian concern. In this context it will be interesting to see what efforts the Soviet Union will be prepared to make to counter the Reagan administration's expansion of the US Navy to a 600-ship force. Soviet air power too has always remained in the shadow of the land forces. The tactical air forces of Frontal Aviation (*Frontovaya aviatsiya*) have always formed the backbone of the Soviet air force and their operations have been rigidly subordinated to those of the land armies. Until the major air reorganizations of the early 1980s each Soviet land army had its own supporting air army and since that time the land and air forces have been even more closely integrated. Thus although the air force is an independent service, its major preoccupation is the support of ground operations. There is no strong Soviet tradition of independent air operations, such as that which exists in the United States Air Force or the Royal Air Force in Britain.

Another peculiarity of Soviet military doctrine which can be traced to the influence of the Russian environment is the classification of military science into tactics (*taktika*), operational art (*operativnoe iskusstvo*) and strategy (*strategiya*). Operational art, which has no equivalent in the English military lexicon, is concerned with action at army and army group level. Strategy deals with the affairs of theaters of operations and higher concerns, while tactics are the province of regiments and divisions.

It is the sheer scale of Soviet military operations which has necessitated the development of this additional dimension of military thinking. The Soviet armed forces appear to be dominated by their environment in other ways. Unlike Western military forces, most notably the United States Air Force with its Red Flag and Aggressor programs, Soviet forces have tended to train to fight themselves rather than a potential enemy. It is easier than may be supposed for military forces which lack recent large-scale combat experience to tailor their training to the demands of peacetime exercises. As the vast and relatively flat expanses of the Western Soviet Union are the Soviet forces' main training area, it is over such terrain that they will operate most efficiently. Even country 1600ft to 3300ft above sea level is defined as mountainous terrain by Soviet military doctrine and as such necessitates special tactics. This point is made primarily to illustrate the distinctive Soviet view of warfare, not to suggest that the Soviet forces will necessarily operate any less effectively because of such attitudes.

The Soviet historical experience is consciously a strong formative influence on Soviet military doctrine. Much of the discussion of current military problems in the unclassified military journals is illustrated by examples of experience during the Great Patriotic War. The former C-in-C of the Soviet air force, Chief Marshal of Aviation Pavel S. Kutakhov (himself a veteran of World War II) wrote that the Great Patriotic War is a vast reservoir of strategic wisdom particularly for air commanders dealing with the application of air power to contemporary military problems. Historical experience reinforces the tendency to accord land warfare a primary position, although developments in modern technology have modified this tendency

to the extent that the Strategic Rocket Force now ranks above even the Army in terms of Soviet military precedence.

Historical experience is, however, often an ambiguous guide to current military concerns. Whereas the Revolutionary fervor of the inter-war years in the Soviet Union tended to produce innovative solutions to military problems, the experience of the Great Patriotic War has helped to reinforce conservative attitudes. This is nowhere more apparent than in the Soviet experience with strategic bomber forces. In the early 1930s a strong strategic bomber force was created, equipped with Tupolev's TB-3 four-engined bomber which was one of the most advanced aircraft of its day. Heavy bomber brigades were grouped within the Special Purpose Air Arm (*Aviatsiya osobovo naznacheniya*) under the command of General Vasili Khripin. A close associate of the reforming army commander Marshal Mikhail Tukhachevski, Khripin was a strong advocate of strategic bombing operations. However, both men together with all Soviet officers who showed any tendency towards originality of mind were liquidated in Stalin's purges of the late 1930s. As a consequence, although a small strategic bomber force survived during the war years as the *Aviatsiya dal'nego deystviya* (Long Range Aviation), beyond a few raids on Berlin of symbolic rather than material value only tactical bombing was carried out by the Soviet air forces during 1941-45. Today the Soviet air force's strategic bombers are of considerably less importance than the ICBMs of the Strategic Rocket Forces. Conversely, airborne forces which were pioneered by the Soviet armed forces

LEFT AND BELOW: The Mikoyan MiG-21, the most widely used combat aircraft in the world in the 1970s, is flown not only by the Soviet Union and Warsaw Pact but in Finland, the Middle East and Asia.

BELOW: MiG-21 pilots liaise before a training sortie. The delta-wing interceptor has proved one of the more durable Soviet jet designs, and continued to add to its quarter-century of service in the mid 1980s.

during the 1930s today form an important element of Soviet military power

A respect for the past and its achievements does not blind the Soviet marshals to the benefits of modern technology. Indeed amongst the Soviet military leadership of recent times there is a strong bias towards engineers and technocrats, notably represented by the long-serving former Defense Minister Marshal Dmitri Ustinov (a civilian defense production expert, his military rank being *ex officio*) and the Chief of the General Staff Marshal Nikolai Ogarkov. On Ustinov's death in December 1984, he was replaced by Marshal of the Soviet Union Sergei Sokolov.

Earlier in the same year, the outspoken and ambitious Ogarkov had fallen from favor, most probably because of a serious disagreement with his political masters over the allocation of defense resources, and in September 1984 he was replaced as Chief of the General Staff by Marshal of the Soviet Union Sergei Akhromeyev. However, Ogarkov's considerable military talents have not been wasted, as he remains a member of the Main Military Council and has special responsibility for the forces facing Western Europe.

There is tremendous pride in Soviet technology. This tendency can be illustrated by two recent Soviet technological achievements: the operational deployment of an ASAT (anti-satellite) system ahead of the West and the introduction of cold launch systems for land-based ICBMs. In terms of pure research, there can be no doubt that the Soviet Union still lags appreciably behind the United States. However, this disadvantage is often offset by a greater willingness to apply new technology to military systems in the Soviet Union.

ABOVE: A Sukhoi Su-17 Fitter-C strike fighter takes off over a radar antenna on the perimeter airfield.

TOP: The MiG-21bis Fishbed-L appeared in 1976 and is one of the more refined versions of the interceptor to see service. A Finnish example is pictured. ABOVE: An interceptor pilot in the cockpit. As elsewhere in the Soviet armed forces, individual pilots are not encouraged to use their initiative, relying mainly on the instructions of their ground controllers.

There is tremendous pride in Soviet technological achievement throughout Soviet society, but in military circles this is not unmixed with apprehension about the Western lead in military technology. However, because of the priority given in the Soviet Union to the armed forces in research and development, as well as in production resources, the gap between East and West as indicated by equipment actually in service is narrower than it might be. This tendency can be illustrated by two recent Soviet technological achievements: the operational deployment of an ASAT (anti-satellite) system ahead of the West and the introduction of cold launch systems for land-based ICBMs. In terms of pure research, there can be no doubt that the Soviet Union still lags appreciably behind the United States. However, this disadvantage is often

offset by a greater willingness to apply new technology to military systems in the Soviet Union.

In spite of Soviet appreciation of the importance of technology, the weapons produced for the Soviet forces often lack refinement. Their ruggedness and simplicity, often mistaken for crudeness, is the result of a deliberate design policy which eschews all unnecessary complexity. A Soviet weapon, whether it be an assault rifle or an air superiority fighter aircraft, is designed first and foremost, of course, to carry out a military task. However, ease of production and ease of maintenance are also important requirements, the latter especially so in a largely conscript-manned service. Therefore, new technology is only introduced when it provides the sole solution to a designer's problems. Otherwise existing equipment will be modified to undertake new tasks. An excellent example of this process is provided by the design and development history of the MiG-21. This aircraft first entered Soviet air force service in 1959 in the MiG-21F (NATO codename Fishbed-C) version, which undertook the clear-weather, point-defense interception mission. Thereafter the basic design was progressively improved to give the fighter an all-weather operating capability and to allow it to carry out ground-attack missions as a secondary duty. Specialized versions were also produced for tactical reconnaissance and for conversion training. In all a dozen major variants have been produced and the latest

MiG-21bis (Fishbed-N) fighter remains in production for the Soviet air force and for export. Frontal Aviation currently operates over a thousand MiG-21s in the air superiority fighter and tactical reconnaissance roles, a quarter of a century after the type first entered service. Although the latest version differs quite considerably from the MiG-21F, because changes have been introduced incrementally, there has never been a serious interruption in the flow of fighters from the Mikoyan production line to operational units.

Perhaps the most frequently stressed military dictum in Soviet defense literature is the primacy of offensive action. If the Soviet armed forces go to war, their aim will be to achieve a swift and overwhelming victory over enemy forces. Such a victory will be all the more necessary if the opponent is armed with nuclear weapons, as it will be the Soviet aim to achieve a decisive conventional victory before such weapons can be used. Clearly once Soviet forces have penetrated into enemy defensive positions and are intermingled with the defenders, they will offer a poor target for tactical nuclear strikes. Furthermore, in a war against the NATO powers political agreement amongst the Allies must be reached before nuclear weapons are released to the military commanders. In Soviet eyes this procedure is a serious weakness which can be exploited by vigorous military action against the

ABOVE: An early demonstration of Soviet helicopter mobility at Tushino in 1956; the Mil Mi-4 rotorcraft leaving the 'battlefield' have just landed troops to reinforce the artillery below them.

weaker members of the Alliance, coupled with political action aimed at suborning their allegiance. Therefore, while Soviet commanders cannot be absolutely confident that nuclear weapons will not be employed against their forces, they must recognize that a ruthlessly applied Blitzkrieg-style offensive represents their best chance of victory.

Soviet military doctrine requires that offensive operations be carried out at high speed and the momentum of advance be maintained at all costs. All available forces must cooperate to ensure that the main objectives are attained, and recent organizational changes in the command structure of tactical air forces will ensure extremely close co-ordination of ground and air action – at any rate in theory.

Whereas in the past, Frontal Aviation was organized into air armies (an arrangement first introduced into the Soviet Air Force in 1942), from the early 1980s tactical air forces have become much more closely integrated with the ground forces that they will support. For example at theater level each Commander-in-Chief of the five Soviet TVDs or theaters of military operations now has a deputy commander for Frontal Aviation and similarly at a lower level the army commanders of the 16 military districts and four groups of Soviet forces have deputy commanders for tactical aviation. The co-operative effort of all forces will be concentrated on points of breakthrough and it is axiomatic that Soviet commanders will reinforce success rather than contribute additional forces to areas where the attack has stalled. Aggressive action on the part of all forces is a necessary prerequisite of victory – both on the ground and in the air.

In the Soviet view, one of the great strengths of their military system is the strict control exercised by the high command over subordinate forces. Such control, it is argued, will ensure that the armed forces will perform like a well-oiled machine in carrying out the carefully-laid plans of the commander. Individual initiative amongst subordinates is not encouraged or valued in the Soviet forces, as it is in Western military organizations. However, the dangers of enemy action knocking out or severely degrading the effectiveness of the command and control system on which centrally-directed action depends is recognized by Soviet military theoreticians. The West has made no secret of its efforts to develop effective electronic countermeasures equipment and strategies aimed at denying Soviet forces their means of electronic battlefield intelligence-gathering and communications. Yet the answer to this threat in the Soviet view is to be found in such technical means as ECCM (electronic counter-countermeasures), careful advanced briefing of forces to minimize the need for communication in action and wherever possible communication by pre-arranged visual signals between forces in contact. Whether such measures will be sufficient to maintain command and control over Soviet forces in the face of intense ECM jamming and deception activity is debatable. The Soviet General Staff apparently believes that a certain degree of initiative at junior command levels will be essential in the future, yet in view of the Soviet military and political tradition of rigid subordination to higher authority this will be difficult to introduce to the limited degree envisaged. In truth the Soviet military command is faced with a genuine dilemma in seeking to solve the problems it will be faced with if its command and control system should happen to break down in battle.

BELOW: Mil Mi-8 Hip assault transports demonstrate how armed troops can be landed. Some 1500 Hips fly with Frontal Aviation, working closely with ground forces wherever they serve.

Careful planning of military operations is a major element in Soviet military doctrine and it may go some way toward solving the problems of loss of communications. Among Soviet conscripts and reservists recalled to active duty in time of crisis the level of military skills will be low. Indeed in many cases conscripts from the Central Asian Soviet Socialist Republics will not even be able to speak Russian and this problem will increase in future as the Russian element of the Soviet Union's population declines, while the non-Russian races grow in numbers. However, the lack of military knowledge at the lowest levels is counterbalanced by the very high level of professional competence achieved by the officer corps. The Soviet officer will certainly have devoted more of his career to military education than his Western counterpart by the time

such considerations in no way temper the draconian discipline which is such a conspicuous feature of Soviet military life. There is none of the free-and-easy comradeship between officers and men which is often to be found in Western armed forces. Officers are formal and often harsh when dealing with their men and relations between officers of different rank are similarly unbending. In time of war serious breaches of military discipline will be punished by execution before a firing squad and officers at all levels of command are likely to be severely punished for lapses on behalf of subordinates. The recriminations following the 'Whiskey on the rocks' affair when a Soviet Whiskey class diesel-electric submarine grounded in Swedish territorial waters in October 1981 even resulted in the removal of the Chief of the Main Naval Staff, Admiral G M Egorov

ABOVE: A Western Frontier District air base entertains local schoolchildren. Indoctrination of Soviet youth occurs from an early age, when they are encouraged to identify with the armed forces. The helicopter is a Mil Mi-8, the officer on the right an ensign, the second highest non-commissioned officer in the land and air forces.

he reaches senior rank. Nonetheless it is only at the highest levels of command that any Soviet officer will have very much scope for implementing original ideas, much less reforms. In general, 'off the peg' solutions derived from the military manuals are preferred to innovation and, again in Soviet eyes, this is a strength of the system. Certainly in such a large organization as the Soviet armed forces there is as much to be gained in operational and tactical flexibility by standardization of thought as there is by commonality of equipment.

The morale of Soviet servicemen is seen as an important factor in their performance and this aspect of military preparedness is the particular concern of the Air Force's Political Directorate. Yet

from his post. Conversely no such witch hunt followed the shooting down of Korean Airlines Flight KAL 007, because all personnel involved carried out their orders effectively. Indeed their action has been commended by no less an authority than Marshal Ogarkov, then Soviet Chief of the General Staff. Such attitudes to discipline are deeply ingrained in Soviet society and indeed in Russian history, as the Tsars were the last European rulers to abolish serfdom. They represent a further inhibiting factor in the development of individual initiative within the armed forces.

Perhaps the realization that in a prolonged conflict with a sophisticated enemy the Soviet command and control system must inevitably begin to

ABOVE: A Soviet Su-15 Flagon interceptor was responsible for the destruction of the Korean Airlines Boeing 747 in September 1983.

LEFT: Then Chief of General Staff Nikolai Ogarkov outlines the incident for the press.

BELOW: A Flagon pilot (right) and groundcrew race to their aircraft.

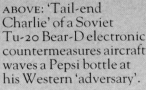

ABOVE: 'Tail-end Charlie' of a Soviet Tu-20 Bear-D electronic countermeasures aircraft waves a Pepsi bottle at his Western 'adversary'.

ABOVE RIGHT: Another Bear-D (recognizable by its chin and belly radar packs) is intercepted on the edge of British airspace by a Royal Air Force Lightning. The Bear was spying on a 1974 NATO naval exercise.

break down – leading to a loss of momentum in the advance and possibly allowing the enemy to gain the initiative – is as important a factor in shaping the Soviet Blitzkrieg technique as is the fear of nuclear weapons. As well as stressing the need for a swift and aggressive offensive, Soviet military doctrine requires that surprise be achieved and that operations be conducted deep in the enemy rear from the outset of hostilities. Modern reconnaissance techniques make it particularly difficult to conceal a build-up of men and matériel from the enemy, but the Soviet forces have a long tradition of the successful employment of deception techniques. In the Great Patriotic War, for example, the construction of dummy airfields to confuse German reconnaissance was commonplace and the deception was often carried to the point where a number of sorties would be flown from the dummy fields to lend credence to their ostensible role. During the build-up before the

great tank battle of Kursk in the summer of 1943, one dummy airfield was built for every three real airstrips constructed.

Concern with deception techniques persists in the Soviet armed forces today, with overall responsibility for strategic deception (in Russian *maskirovka*) in the hands of a Chief Directorate of the General Staff under a Marshal of the Soviet Union. Present-day techniques of *maskirovka* are considerably more sophisticated than those of World War II and include such technical measures as reserving certain operating frequencies of electronic equipment for wartime use only, so that the enemy can gain no prior knowledge of them through ELINT (electronic intelligence) aircraft or satellites. Perhaps more effective in the initial stages of a conflict will be attempts to disguise the significance of military movements from the enemy, for example by passing them off as training maneuvers or internal

security measures. In Central Europe NATO's defense depends to a large degree upon the timely decision to reinforce troops in the theater and to move forces within the region from peacetime barracks to forward defensive positions. Consequently any delay that Soviet techniques of deception can gain in the implementation of NATO's deployment and reinforcement plans will considerably assist the Soviet forces in achieving surprise (*vnezapnost*) in their initial assault.

Operations deep into enemy territory have several important objectives, including the capture or destruction of tactical nuclear weapons and their delivery systems, the elimination of command centers and of such command and control systems as air surveillance radars, the neutralization of enemy air power by attacks on airfields and the general weakening of both military and civilian morale which such action will engender. The forces employed on these operations will include bomber aircraft such as the Tupolev Tu-26 Backfire, more specialized interdiction aircraft such as the Sukhoi Su-24 Fencer and ground forces of various kinds, including airborne troops (perhaps in divisional strength), heliborne assault troops, and small groups of GRU (Soviet military intelligence) *Spetsnaz* troops, the equivalent of the US Army's Special Forces. In addition to these essentially diversionary raiding forces, the Soviet army plans to launch Operational Maneuver Groups of divisional strength or larger on forays deep into NATO territory. Their objective will not be to engage and defeat enemy forces, but to contribute to the destruction of vital installations and the undermining of Western morale. What is particularly noteworthy about these plans for disruption of enemy rear areas is the close integration of air and ground action. Not only will the air interdiction effort be complemented by the raids of ground forces, but in some cases target identification and designation for attacking aircraft will be undertaken by ground teams. Similarly ground forces will depend on the air force for transport to their parachute drop zones or helicopter landing zones and thereafter for fire support. This is a further illustration of the practical application of the Soviet 'all arms' philosophy, which seeks to coordinate the efforts of all forces to achieve the main strategic aims. Cooperation between air and ground forces, at least in theory, has reached the point in the Soviet armed forces where air operations represent a natural extension of the battle on the ground into a third dimension.

Much of this chapter has been concerned with the

hand, comparisons with Western practice can be somewhat misleading, because Soviet equipment is designed to be simple and straightforward to service and operate. Consequently, Soviet aircraft can be maintained by personnel with much lower levels of skill than that required for equivalent Western aircraft. This was discovered by the Egyptian air force, when it began to introduce American F-4 Phantom fighter-bombers into service in 1979. Having previously operated such Soviet types as the MiG-21 and MiG-23, the Egyptians found the F-4s very difficult to maintain. In comparison with the MiG-21 which required 22 maintenance man hours per flight hour, the F-4 needed 45 maintenance man hours per flight hour. This would tend to confirm that Soviet designers succeed in producing aircraft

BELOW: Soviet paratroops land in Byelorussia in one of the frequent exercises designed to coordinate air and land forces.

Soviet theory of war. However, the crucial question of whether the Soviet armed forces have personnel of sufficient technical skill and with the necessary motivation to enable them to translate these concepts into effective military action cannot be ignored. As has already been suggested, the high quality that is evident in Soviet military thought and planning is generally not matched by the caliber of conscript service personnel. As the air force relies on the professional officer caste for its pilots, the poor technical skills and lack of motivation of conscript forces will not directly affect its efficiency on operations. However, these shortcomings may become apparent through high aircraft unserviceability rates and a consequent weakening of air strength under the pressures of intense air operations. Soviet air regiments do not have the same opportunity for practicing the skills required for intensive air operations as for example does the USAF's tactical fighter force with its 'sortie surge' exercises. This is a matter of deliberate Soviet policy, as in general the Soviet forces attempt to conserve equipment for use in action rather than subjecting it to wear-and-tear during anything but the minimum of essential training. On the other

FISHBEDS WITH MISSILES UNDER WINGS

AA-2 (███) AM

ABOVE: Fishbeds in Cuba! The presence of Soviet combat types in Central America in 1962 almost precipitated an armed confrontation between the two superpowers.

LEFT: Students at Frunze Military Academy watch intently as Major General Alexei Prokhorov instructs them on the finer points of the MiG-25 Foxbat.

with maintenance requirements well matched to the skills of the Soviet conscript.

As the Soviet air force lacks recent combat experience on any appreciable scale against a sophisticated enemy, it is difficult to assess the level of flying skill and combat proficiency attained by its aircrew. However, it is known that a Soviet pilot will accumulate some 120 flying hours on average per year. This compares unfavorably with the yearly average of 210 hours currently flown by the pilots of the USAF's Tactical Air Command and it is well below the NATO requirement of 240 flying hours per year for combat pilots. Although Soviet air regiments in general operate their aircraft with less frequency than do NATO air units, this is partly the result of the policy whereby flying hours are conserved to permit a higher state of readiness for wartime operations. One of the three squadrons in a typical Frontal Aviation fighter regiment will be responsible for peacetime training and will be allocated a number of two-seat conversion trainers as well as single-seat fighter types. Flying training activity generally reaches a peak during the summer, when the Soviet pilot can expect to fly for 20 hours each month, but at other times his monthly flying hours may be as low as five. The Soviet tactical pilot receives less weapons training before first joining an operational unit than does his Western counterpart and thereafter his regiment's participation in large scale air exercises will be only infrequent. However, the Soviet pilot's limited flying time is to some degree compensated for by a more intensive course of training than is usual in Western air arms.

One of the essential differences between the Soviet and NATO approaches to tactical air power is that, whereas the Western fighter units are expected to maintain a steady sortie rate over a period of several weeks, the Soviet air regiment will operate intensively for a short period (typically five days) and thereafter will rapidly fall-off in effectiveness. This difference can readily be seen by comparing the numbers of support personnel required per combat aircraft by the Soviet air force and a NATO air arm. The Air Forces of the Group of Soviet Forces in Germany require around seventy personnel to support one aircraft, whereas the corresponding figure for the West German Luftwaffe is 250 personnel. The Soviet Frontal Aviation unit, like the Soviet army division, is essentially tailored to fight the short and intense battles which will characterize the opening days of a major war. With a force of over 5000 tactical combat aircraft in service, the Soviet Air Force can bring great numbers of warplanes into action early in a conflict. During exercises as many as 2400 machines have been involved in an air operation and NATO commanders anticipate wave attacks on key targets by as many as 400 aircraft.

Soviet commanders are taught to be realistic in their planning and to ensure that no operation is undertaken with forces insufficient to accomplish it. If this rigorous standard is applied to the Soviet armed forces as a whole, set against the tasks that they will have to undertake in a major war, it can be seen that they represent a powerful tool well adapted to implement the dictates of the Kremlin's policy.

CHAPTER TWO

THE ORGANIZATION OF AIR POWER

PREVIOUS PAGES: Tupolev Tu-16 Badger bombers of the Northern Fleet perform a mid-air refueling maneuver.
ABOVE: Although Mikhail Gorbachev acceded to the Soviet leadership in March 1985, he did not immediately assume chairmanship of the Defense Council.
ABOVE RIGHT: Marshal of the Soviet Union Sergei Akhromeyev, who succeeded Nikolai Ogarkov as Chief of the General Staff in 1984.

At the apex of the Soviet military command structure is the Defense Council. The Council's exact composition is not known, but it is likely to include the Defense Minister, Foreign Minister, Chairman of the KGB, Minister for the Interior, Minister for the Defense Industries and Chairman of the Council of Ministers. It is believed that its only permanent military member is the Chief of the General Staff, Marshal Akhromeyev, but that other military members, such as the Commander-in-Chief of the Warsaw Pact, may take part in certain of the Council's deliberations. The Council is responsible in peacetime for the determining of long-term defense policy goals and for ensuring that industrial capacity and manpower are made available to implement these programs. It will also of course be able to assume the tasks of wartime strategic direction with no alteration or augmentation of its resources. The late President Chernenko was also chairman of the Defense Council – and, though his successor Mikhail Gorbachev did not immediately assume that position, he was expected to do so in due course.

Command and administration of the Soviet armed forces is the responsibility of the Ministry of

RIGHT: Current Minister of Defense Sergei Sokolov, pictured while deputizing for then-minister Ustinov in the November 1984 Red Square parade.
FAR RIGHT: Ustinov's predecessor, Marshal Grechko, was more typical of those in the position by virtue of his previous experience as a military officer.

Defense, to which the five services which make up the Soviet military machine are subordinated. The Ministry's chief command functions are exercised through the Main Military Council, which is chaired by the Minister of Defense and includes the senior Soviet commanders, chiefs of technical and support services and the Chief of the General Staff. Sergei Sokolov, the present Minister of Defense, is assisted by the First Deputy Ministers, all of them military officers. Indeed Sokolov's predecessor, Ustinov, was unusual in being a civilian defense production expert, elevated to the military rank of Marshal. Traditionally the Defense Minister's post has been filled by a senior military officer. Ustinov's predecessor Marshal A A Grechko distinguished himself as an army commander during the Great Patriotic War and then held the posts of C-in-C of Ground Forces and C-in-C of the Warsaw Pact, before becoming Defense Minister. The present Minister of Defense, Marshal Sokolov, joined the Soviet Army in 1932 and saw action against the Germans and the Finns during the Great Patriotic War. He subsequently rose to command the Leningrad Military District, before his appointment to the Main Military Council as First Deputy Minister of Defense for General Affairs in 1967.

Ustinov's appointment as Minister of Defense in 1976 signalled a recognition of the importance of technology and industrial capacity in Soviet military strength. During the Khrushchev era relations between the armed forces and the Soviet political leadership had often been stormy. The marshals resented Khrushchev's interference in military affairs and they inevitably found the reduction in strength of the massive Soviet ground forces and the new emphasis on strategic rocket forces a painful transition. Since the mid 1960s the relations between the civilian leadership and the armed forces had noticeably improved. Brezhnev was warm in his praise of the armed forces and his high regard for the military was shown by the myth of his wartime service.

Although his successors Andropov and Chernenko – and now Gorbachev – are very different men, there is no sign that the harmonious accord between the party leadership and the armed forces has ended. This is not to suggest that the armed

forces have ever seriously challenged the primacy of the Communist Party's leadership, even during Khrushchev's turbulent years in power. It is rather to emphasise that for the past two decades the Communist Party and Soviet armed forces have been in very close agreement about the scope and direction of the State's military expansion.

The detailed planning and implementation of military policy is carried out within the Ministry of Defense by the General Staff. The Chief of the General Staff, at present Marshal Akhromeyev, is one of the most influential officers in the Soviet military hierarchy. Ogarkov was a close associate of Ustinov and, like the late Minister of Defense, he is an engineer by training. After service with a military

ABOVE: Chief of the Main Political Directorate A A Yepishev, an *ex-officio* member of the Main Military Council.

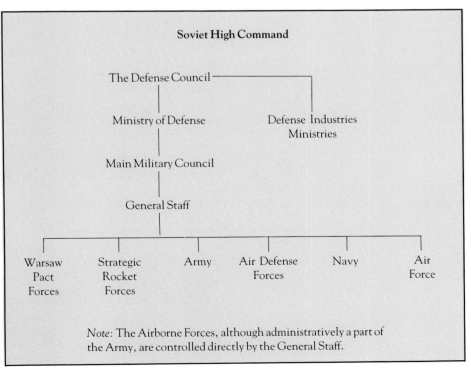

Soviet High Command

The Defense Council

Ministry of Defense — Defense Industries Ministries

Main Military Council

General Staff

Warsaw Pact Forces | Strategic Rocket Forces | Army | Air Defense Forces | Navy | Air Force

Note: The Airborne Forces, although administratively a part of the Army, are controlled directly by the General Staff.

ABOVE: Warsaw Pact Commander-in-Chief Viktor Kulikov (center) inspects troops during exercises in Poland. The host country's Prime Minister General Jaruzelski (left) and Defense Minister Florian Siwicki look on.

engineer unit in the Great Patriotic War, Ogarkov qualified as a staff officer and rose to command a Soviet military district. It is unusual for a technical specialist to receive such an appointment even in Western armed forces, and this indicates that Ogarkov is an officer of exceptional ability. In 1968 he joined the General Staff as a first deputy chief with special responsibility for strategic nuclear weapons policy and planning and in 1977 became Chief of the General Staff, a post carrying the political rank of first deputy minister of defense. In the early 1980s Ogarkov had been responsible for a major restructuring of Soviet tactical forces which has greatly improved their readiness for war. Notably, the tactical air support and air defense units have been more closely integrated with the ground force formations that they will support; the emphasis on command at front level (in wartime the 16 Soviet military districts will become fronts) has shifted to operations on a larger scale by the five TVDs or theaters of military operations; and there has been a greater willingness to experiment in tailoring ground/air force groupings to meet the needs of specific military missions. Ogarkov's reforms had largely been implemented by the time of his dismissal in September 1984. Nonetheless, his retention on the Main Military Council is an indication of the Soviet leadership's regard for his military abilities, although this is doubtless tempered by some distrust of his political reliability.

The close relationship between the Communist Party of the Soviet Union and the armed forces is fostered by the Ministry of Defense's political directorate. Political officers are assigned to all units and headquarters down to regimental level and political instruction is a regular feature of Soviet military training. The great majority of Soviet officers (over 90 percent) are Communist Party members or they belong to Komsomol, the Party's youth organization. The political reliability and security of the armed forces is further ensured by assigning a branch of the KGB to watch over the services. However, despite the presence of political deputies with all units, the days of divided command between military commanders and political commisars are long past. The political officer's duties and responsibilities are well defined; in addition to his work of political education he carries out a useful function as a welfare officer and as a barometer of unit morale.

The five branches of the Soviet armed forces come under the direct operational control of the General Staff. They are the Strategic Rocket Forces, the Army, the Air Defense Forces, the Air Force and the Navy. In addition, the Soviet airborne forces, although organizationally a part of the Army, are directly subordinated to the General Staff. Furthermore the General Staff exercises command over the military forces of the Soviet Union's Warsaw Pact allies, through the agency of Commander-in-Chief Warsaw Pact forces. This post is invariably filled by a senior Soviet Officer (at present this is Marshal V G Kulikov) and ranks second in importance to that of the Chief of the General Staff. The Strategic Rocket Forces, which controls all Soviet

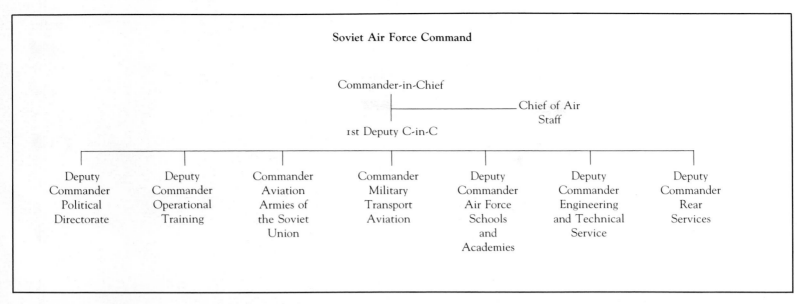

Soviet Air Force Command

land-based strategic missiles, ranks first in precedence amongst the Soviet forces. This service was formed on 7 May 1960 and at present it controls six operational rocket armies. The SRF is commanded by Chief Marshal of Artillery V F Tolubko, who has held this post since 1972.

The Air Defense Forces is a somewhat older service, having been formed in 1954. It is at present organized into five major air defense districts, corresponding with the theaters of military operations. In addition to the service's responsibilities for the defense of Soviet airspace, the Air Defense Forces also covers the territory of the Warsaw Pact allies and it controls all Army air defense troops. The responsibilities of the Army do not extend to the control of military helicopters, which are operated by the Air Force on their behalf. The Army's 1,800,000 troops are commanded through the five theaters of military operations with the 16 military districts of the Soviet Union and Groups of Soviet Forces in eastern Europe providing a lower level of command. The four Groups of Soviet Forces comprise the Group of Soviet Forces in Germany, the Northern Group in Poland, the Central Group in Czechoslovakia and the Southern Group in Hungary. The Navy is organized into four fleets, each of which has its own Naval Air Force component which is provided by the Air Force. The fleets are the Northern Fleet, the Baltic Fleet, the Black Sea Fleet and the Pacific Fleet.

The non-Soviet members of the Warsaw Pact contribute an additional 55 Army divisions and 2240 tactical aircraft to the Soviet forces deployed in Central and Eastern Europe. The armed forces of Bulgaria, Czechoslovakia, East Germany, Hungary, Poland and Romania are trained to fight using Soviet tactics and are for the most part equipped with Soviet weaponry. As a result, they are for most practical purposes interchangeable with Soviet forces, except that their reliability and loyalty must be open to question in a Soviet-inspired conflict. All non-Soviet Warsaw Pact forces have advisers from the Soviet armed forces attached to them and in the cases of East Germany, Poland, Czechoslovakia and Hungary, Soviet forces are stationed on their territory. The integration of Soviet and non-Soviet forces within the Warsaw Pact has been closest in the case of air defense units, as the allies contribute forces to the Soviet Air Defense Forces, rather than having national air defense organizations of their own. Needless to say these forces are

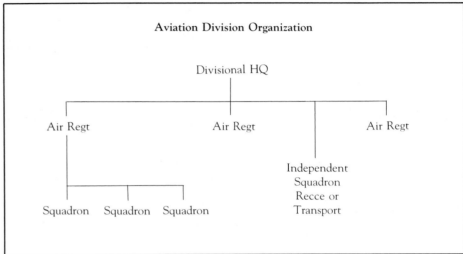

Aviation Division Organization

under Soviet command. In general the equipment of the Pact allies is less modern than that of Soviet forces. This is especially true of the so-called 'southern tier' states (Hungary, Romania and Bulgaria). The East German forces are unusual in that they are directly subordinated to the Group of Soviet Forces in Germany.

The theaters of military operations or TVDs (*teatr voennykh deistvii*), have become an important feature of Soviet military organization in the past few years. They provide a higher level of command than that at front or military district level and allow both a closer integration of land and air forces and also a more flexible grouping of forces within the area of command than that possible at front level. The five TVDs are Central Europe, South-West Europe, North Europe, South and Far East. The most important area of deployment for Soviet tactical forces is the Western theater, with 30 Army divisions in Central and Eastern Europe, a further 65 divisions in the western military districts of the Soviet Union and a central strategic reserve of 16 divisions in the Moscow area. Frontal Aviation strength in this region comprises over 3600 tactical aircraft. In the Southern theater there are 29 divisions, supported by 845 tactical aircraft, and this theater is responsible for operations in Afghanistan. The Far Eastern theater controls 52 divisions and a tactical air force of over 1700 aircraft.

In Western Europe the Soviet Union is faced with the forces of the NATO alliance, which its forces substantially outnumber. For example there are four

ABOVE: Three MiG-21s complete a low-level pass for the benefit of spectators on the occasion of the 50th anniversary of the October Revolution in 1967.
RIGHT: A Fishbed-L variant of the MiG-21 in East German service.

million Warsaw Pact troops deployed in the theater, organized into 173 divisions, while NATO's ground forces number 2.6 million in 84 divisions. The Pact's superiority in main battle tanks (42,500 to 13,000) and in artillery pieces (31,500 to 10,750) is immense. In tactical air power too the Warsaw Pact has the edge in aircraft actually deployed in the region (7240 compared with NATO's 2975), although this advantage can be swiftly lost as air reinforcements are flown in from the United States. Transatlantic reinforcement is the key to a successful NATO defense of Western Europe on the ground as well as in the air. This strategy tends to confirm the Soviet belief in the need for a swift conventional assault, so that the war can be decided before these reinforcements can be deployed. However, it is primarily the fear of nuclear weapons which has determined Soviet strategy, as the Soviet planners believe a swift result will give NATO little time to reach agreement on nuclear release. The NATO policy of forward defense (decided on for political reasons, despite strong military arguments against it, to reassure West Germany that her territory will not be lightly abandoned) gives the Soviet forces a further incentive to seek a quick conventional victory through Blitzkrieg-style assault tactics.

In the Southern theater strong Soviet forces have the capability of direct military intervention in the Middle East region and especially in the increasingly-unstable Persian Gulf area. However, since December 1979 the forces of this theater have been heavily committed to counter-insurgency opera-

tions in Afghanistan. More than 105,000 troops supported by tactical aircraft and some 500 helicopters are engaged in a bitterly-fought guerrilla war with Afghan tribesmen, for which Soviet forces are both ill-trained and unsuitably equipped. The Afghanistan involvement considerably reduces the likelihood of Soviet forces attempting to occupy the Iranian oilfields. Yet in the longer-term view this strategic option could prove to be attractive to the Soviet leadership, as it offers a possible solution to the serious oil shortages which it is forecast the Soviet Union will face by the end of the century. The Soviet Union, of course, does not lack immense energy resources of its own, but it is deficient in the technological skills needed to exploit them. Should the necessary assistance to develop Siberia's mineral wealth not be forthcoming from Western Europe and Japan (as the United States has urged on its allies), then a military solution to the energy problem could be attempted. Little stands in the way of a Soviet occupation of Iran, as that state's forces have notably failed to match their Islamic fervor with military skill during the long drawn-out war with neighboring Iraq. As in Western Europe, the United States could only counter such a move by reinforcing the area by air and sealift. In terms of military strength, therefore, the Soviet Union is in a particularly strong position along her southern borders, especially since the forces in this theater are in general equipped with modern equipment. Indeed it is with this theater's tactical air forces that the new Sukhoi Su-25 (NATO Frogfoot) has been first deployed for operational trials in Afghanistan.

In the Far East the Soviet Union is faced with a hostile People's Republic of China, which is in some respects a *de facto* ally of the United States. This raises the specter for the Soviet forces of war on two widely-separated fronts. Although the Chinese armed forces are immense, with more than four

million servicemen under arms, they are in general poorly equipped with 1950s-vintage weaponry. The air force has a front-line strength of some 5300 combat aircraft, but the majority of these are Chinese-built versions of the MiG-17 and MiG-19 fighters which were retired from Soviet service more than a decade ago. However, one element of Chinese military power which must be viewed with more respect by the Soviet marshals is the small strategic force of nuclear-armed medium bombers (Chinese-built Tupolev Tu-16s) and land and submarine-based ballistic missiles. The Chinese nuclear stockpile is believed to consist of several hundred

tactical and strategic warheads and the Chinese have delivery systems capable of targeting most of Soviet territory. An anti-Soviet China therefore presents the Soviet Union with a potentially serious military threat in the Far Eastern theater.

A further complication of the military balance of forces in the region could arise from a rejuvenation of Japan's defense forces. Since World War II Japan has eschewed an active military strategy and has preferred to shelter beneath an American nuclear and conventional umbrella, while providing only for a minimum level of national defense. However, Soviet military expansion in the Far East and es-

ABOVE: Myasishchev's speedy but little-used Mya-4 Bison bomber in flight.
TOP LEFT: A Tu-26 Backfire climbs away with its variable geometry wing in an unswept position.
LEFT: A venerable Tu-20 Bear-D lumbers across Northern skies.

pecially the forward deployment of naval forces which has been made possible by the Soviet Union's alliance with Vietnam has caused considerable concern in Japan. The Japanese fear that Soviet naval action in the South China Sea could cut them off both from their sources of essential raw materials, notably Middle East oil, and also from the overseas markets. Nearer to the Japanese homeland Soviet naval and air forces appear to be seeking control of the Sea of Japan and to the north the Soviet military build-up in the Kurile Islands is a further cause for concern. Whether these pressures will be strong enough to overcome the Japanese electorate's re-

pugnance of a revival of national military strength, and also the resistance that such a move would arouse among most Asian nations, is a matter for conjecture. However, the Soviet Union cannot be complacent about the dangers to its security in the region that a Japanese military revival would entail.

With overall command of Soviet tactical forces exercised through the theaters of military operations, one of the main tasks of the air force's organization is to provide well-equipped, well-trained and combat-ready forces for the regional commanders. The primary task of the Air Force (VVS or *Voenno-vozdushnye sili*) is army support, an emphasis that has

ABOVE: Having started life in the 1950s as a bomber, the Tupolev Tu-20 Bear was converted in some numbers to an electronic countermeasures and reconnaissance type (Bear-D illustrated), and was even reinstated in production in 1983.

LEFT: Sukhoi's Su-24 Fencer long-range interdictor was introduced to service in the mid 1970s. It is smaller than, though similar in configuration to, the American F-111.

remained unchanged since the days of the Great Patriotic War in spite of the tremendous advances in Soviet operational and technical capabilities since that time. This being the case, the most important air force subordinate command is Frontal Aviation (FA or *Frontovaya aviatsiya*), which is made up of nearly 6000 tactical combat aircraft and 2300 helicopters. The organization of strategic bombers and theater nuclear strike and interdiction aircraft has recently been radically altered. Until the early 1980s, long-range bombers such as the Tu-20 Bear and Myasishchev Mya-4 Bison, together with medium-range bombers in the class of the Tu-26

Backfire and Tu-16 Badger, belonged to the VVS's Long Range Aviation command (DA, or *Dal'nyaya aviatsiya*). Interdiction aircraft, such as the obsolescent Yakovlev Yak-28 Brewer and the more effective Su-24 Fencer, were operated by Frontal Aviation. However, a completely new organization, the Aviation Armies of the Soviet Union, has emerged in place of Long Range Aviation. The new command combines responsibilities for long and medium-range bomber aircraft, together with that for interdiction aircraft. This reorganization is partly a recognition of the greatly enhanced striking power of the Su-24 Fencer in comparison with the Yak-28.

The Su-24 has a 515 nautical mile radius of action carrying a 5500lb warload, in comparison with the earlier aircraft's 270 nautical mile radius with a 3600lb weapons load. However, it is also an indication of the changing role of the manned bomber in Soviet strategy, with theater air strikes (nuclear and conventional) assuming a greater importance than intercontinental operations.

Air transport is another responsibility of the air force, with the Military Transport Aviation command (VTA or *Voenno-transportnaya aviatsiya*) controlling some 1200 aircraft. About half of this force is made up of medium/long-range cargo transports, such as the Ilyushin Il-76 Candid, Antonov An-12 Cub and An-22 Cock. The remainder are shorter-range communications and personnel transports. In time of crisis – and indeed often on peacetime overseas-deployment flights – the resources of the Military Transport Aviation fleet are augmented

BELOW: The two-seat training (U-suffix) version of the Yakovlev Yak-28. NATO code-names for the now-obsolescent type were Firebar (fighter), Brewer (bomber) and Maestro (trainer). Note the MiG-19s in the background.

35

by civil aircraft drawn from the national airline Aeroflot. The civil fleet will almost double the military air lift forces in terms of numbers with some 1100 passenger and cargo transport aircraft. Naval air forces are in a somewhat anomalous position, in that they are provided by the Air Force but come under the operational jurisdiction of the Navy. The Naval Air Force (A-VMF or *Aviatsiya voenno-morskovo flota*) is organized into four fleet air forces to support the Northern, Baltic, Black Sea and Pacific Fleets. In the main its units are land-based, although this situation is gradually changing with the deployment of *Kiev*-class VTOL carriers and fully-capable nuclear-powered strike carriers now in prospect.

An important element of Soviet air power is represented by the interceptor regiments of the Air Defense Forces (PVO, or *Voyska Protivovozdushnaya oborona*). Although a separate service from the Air Force and outranking it in precedence, the two services have close ties in commonality of equipment, training and base facilities. In addition to its aviation regiments, the Air Defense Forces control an extensive network of ground-based radars and command centers, numerous surface-to-air missile batteries and the air defense troops of the armies in the field. The Air Defense Forces are organized into five major commands corresponding with the theaters of military operations, with each military district of the Soviet Union having a deputy commander for air defense to provide an intermediate level of command between the TVDs and the interceptor regiments.

At the top of the Air Force organizational pyra-

RIGHT: The daunting shape of Antonov's mighty An-22 Cock. Each main undercarriage unit consists of three twin-wheel groups housed in the fuselage blister fairings, giving the giant transport rough-field operating capability.

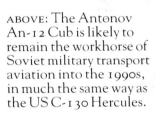

ABOVE: The Antonov An-12 Cub is likely to remain the workhorse of Soviet military transport aviation into the 1990s, in much the same way as the US C-130 Hercules.

LEFT: Similar in configuration to the Lockheed Starlifter, Ilyushin's Il-76 outperforms its Western counterpart by fulfilling both the strategic and operational-tactical transport roles.

BELOW: Chief Marshal of Aviation Pavel S Kutakhov, Air Force C-in-C from 1969-84.
BELOW RIGHT: Forger pilots aboard *Minsk*. Despite the VTOL type's obvious design shortcomings, it adds a valuable fixed-wing capability to the fleet.
BOTTOM: *Kiev* (pictured) and its three sister ships usually carry a complement of 16 Ka-25 ASW helicopters and 14 Forgers.

mid is a military council, chaired by the service's commander-in-chief. This post was held from March 1969 to 1984 by Chief Marshal of Aviation Pavel Stepanovich Kutakhov. During his period of command the Soviet Air Force underwent a significant transformation. During the 1960s Soviet tactical air power was primarily concerned with the air defense of front-line ground forces and their rear areas, with a secondary ground attack mission being undertaken by the fighter aircraft and a few more-specialized attack and light bombers. However, in the course of the 1970s Frontal Aviation acquired both a truly effective dual-role air superiority and ground attack fighter in the MiG-23/27 Flogger and a far-ranging interdiction aircraft with the introduction of the Su-24 Fencer. Thus the Soviet Air Force during the Kutakhov years shifted its emphasis

from a primarily defensive capability to a much more balanced tactical operational doctrine, with due attention accorded to offensive applications of air power in both the close air support of armies and in far-ranging interdiction missions.

The role of individuals in the Soviet high command tends to be greater than that of senior Western officers. This is because the Soviet commanders remain in their posts for long periods, unless forced to relinquish them through ill-health or disgrace. The Western view is that by limiting an officer's tenure of command to a fixed period, typically of four years, promotion channels will not become blocked and the danger of commanders' thinking and decision-making becoming stale and stereotyped is avoided. The Soviet armed forces by contrast value continuity of command and believe that

standardization of operational doctrine is a virtue not a disadvantage of their military system. Kutakhov's fifteen years as C-in-C of the Soviet Air Force was by no means unusual. His predecessor, Chief Marshal of Aviation K A Vershinin served in that post from 1946 until 1969. Kutakhov, unlike the current generation of Western commanders, was a veteran of World War II. He joined the Soviet Air Force in 1935 and qualified as a pilot three years later. He fought with a fighter regiment against Finland during the Winter War of 1939-40 and it was while fighting against the Finnish Air Force on the Karelian Front during the Great Patriotic War that Kutakhov was created a Hero of the Soviet Union in May 1943. His service with an élite Guards fighter regiment was creditable, but by no means outstanding. His combat score of 14 air victories places him well below the Soviet top-scoring ace Ivan Kozhedub and over 800 fighter pilots were credited with 16 or more aerial victories by the Soviet Air Force.

Kutakhov was replaced after his death in 1984 by A N Yefimov, formerly the Soviet Air Force's First Deputy Commander-in-Chief. Another veteran of the Great Patriotic War, during which he was twice decorated as Hero of the Soviet Union, Yefimov flew Ilyushin Il-2 Shturmovik ground-attack aircraft with the 4th Air Army. It is believed that as well as acting as Kutakhov's deputy, Yefimov also commanded the forces of Frontal Aviation. The Chief of the Air Staff, Marshal of Aviation G P Skorikov, is another influential commander, as is the Deputy Commander for Political Administration, Colonel-General of Aviation L L Batekhin. Other Deputy Commanders have special responsibilities for operational training, air force schools and academies, engineering and technical services and rear services. The Commanders of Military Transport Aviation and Aviation Armies of the Soviet Union also rank as Deputy Commanders-in-Chief and have a seat on the Military Council. Naval Aviation, commanded by Colonel-General of Aviation A A Mironenko, is under the operational control of the Navy and so reports to the Naval C-in-C, Admiral of the Fleet S G Gorshkov. However, the Air Force retains a large measure of administrative responsibility for

TOP: A MiG-21F Fishbed-C interceptor of the Finnish Air Force is prepared for flight.
ABOVE: Lieut Col Churilov, a Soviet Navy Forger pilot, signals his readiness for take-off from a land base.

ABOVE: A MiG-23 Flogger takes part in the Warsaw Pact West-81 exercises.

LEFT: A Kamov Ka-25 Hormone of the Soviet Navy overflies HMS *Ark Royal* during an Eastern Atlantic exercise in the mid 1970s. A Buccaneer and Phantom stand on the flight deck.

ABOVE: Sukhoi Su-17 pilots return from a training mission. The variable-geometry Su-17 was developed from the earlier Su-7 and is a considerably more capable aircraft than its fixed-wing predecessor.

Naval Aviation, being responsible for its manning, equipment and various support functions.

The basic flying unit in the Soviet Air Force is the regiment (*polk*), which is generally made up of three squadrons (*eskadrilii*). The regiment is generally equipped with a single aircraft type and trains for a specific role. In some cases squadrons operate independently, for example those undertaking air transport or reconnaissance duties. However, it is more usual for them to form regiments, which are in turn grouped into divisions (*divisiya*). The division is typically made up of three regiments, which will all undertake the same broad mission, for example ground attack, but will not necessarily all fly the same type of aircraft. For example, a division could be composed of two Su-17-equipped regiments and a MiG-27-equipped regiment, all of which have a close air support or battlefield interdiction role. Air transport and reconnaissance squadrons may be attached to a division and a regiment may have its own communications flight, equipped with light transport aircraft or helicopters. The strength of a typical tactical fighter division will be about 150 combat aircraft.

Soviet terminology for tactical air missions does not exactly correspond with Western usage. For example, there is no real equivalent to air accompaniment (*soprovozhdeniye*) in NATO tactical

RIGHT: Admiral Sergei Gorshkov, so-called 'Architect of Soviet Naval Power,' to whom the Colonel-General of Naval Aviation A A Mironenko must report.

doctrine. This role is apparently intended to cover the provision of air support for forces operating deep into enemy territory. These would include both Operational Maneuver Groups, airborne forces and helicopter assault troops. It may also extend to the provision of fighter escort and ground defense suppression (of surface-to-air missiles, anti-aircraft artillery and their directing radars) for interdiction aircraft. Other Soviet terms however are more readily translatable and understandable. They include air defense cover (*prikrytiye*), support (*podderzhka*), reconnaissance (*razvedka*) and airlift (*transportnaya*).

Soviet air power in its widest sense is concerned with both strategic and tactical missions. In the former category, the Strategic Rocket Forces' preparedness for nuclear war at theater level and above is complemented by the Aviation Armies of the Soviet Union manned bomber force. Strategic defense is the primary concern of the Air Defense Forces; and the Naval Air Force's anti-submarine warfare mission and the Military Air Transport long-range airlift mission can also be regarded, at any rate in part, as strategic operations. At the tactical level, air support of the ground forces is the major mission. A Soviet ground offensive would be accompanied by air and anti-air operations. The air operation would be directed in the initial stages of the conflict at the enemy nuclear forces and at his air force. It is unlikely that tactical nuclear weapons would be used for these missions at the outset of hostilities, particularly if this would be likely to trigger reprisal nuclear strikes against Soviet forces. However, it is possible that biological or chemical weapons (most probably the latter) would be widely

LEFT: Paratroops prepare for the signal to drop. Soviet airborne forces would quickly be called upon to reinforce any ground offensive in Western Europe.

ABOVE RIGHT AND RIGHT: Mikoyan MiG-23 Floggers pictured during an official visit to France. The MiG-23 fighter and its MiG-27 attack variant have given the Soviets a dual air-to-air and air-to-ground capability comparable to that afforded by the US F-4 Phantom.

employed. The anti-air operation would be concerned with protecting Soviet air and ground forces from enemy air attack, both by the use of air superiority fighters and by ground-based air defense units. Soviet nuclear warheads and their delivery

RIGHT: Groundcrew load 57mm rockets into a UB-32 pod carried by a Mil Mi-24 Hind attack helicopter.
BELOW: The imposing sight of a fully-armed Hind in flight. This Hind-A variant serves with the GSFG (Group of Soviet Forces in Germany).

systems would be given especially close protection. The overall command of such an operation would be exercised by the C-in-C of the theater of military operations, with his deputy commander for tactical aviation directing the air operation, while the deputy commander for air defense orchestrated the anti-air operation.

Among the missions undertaken by the tactical air forces of Frontal Aviation are large-scale air strikes against enemy rear area targets. Nuclear delivery systems, nuclear storage sites and airfields would be the priority objectives for such air strikes. Other attractive targets are likely to be logistics centers (and especially the depots holding prepositioned equipment for American units which will be flown into the theater of war as emergency reinforcements) and communications targets such as bridges, defiles and potential 'choke points' along the enemy forces' supply lines. Attacks by tactical aircraft are likely to be orchestrated with raids by airborne and heliborne troops (*desants*) and possibly by strikes of tactical missiles armed with chemical warheads. Support of ground forces in contact with the enemy and battlefield interdiction are Frontal Aviation missions which will be closely coordinated with artillery fire support. In general the Soviet ground forces will rely on artillery support whenever this is available and reserve air attacks for targets beyond the reach of the guns or to support raiding forces with insufficient artillery firepower of their own. Soviet armed helicopters will be used in the

close air support role in preference to fixed-wing aircraft, with the latter being reserved for battlefield interdiction targets. However, fixed-wing ground attack aircraft will have an important part to play in preliminary bombardment in preparation for an assault. Tactical air reconnaissance plays a vital role in locating targets for air strike forces.

Airlift operations are generally conducted within the theater of operations to resupply units with such urgently-required stores as ammunition. They will also be used offensively to position raiding parties of airborne troops (perhaps in divisional strength, but often much smaller) behind enemy lines and to keep such forces supplied. A proportion of the air transport force may be used for strategic airlift, for example to fly in reinforcements from military districts in the Soviet interior. The passenger-carrying transports of Aeroflot would be particularly suitable for this role.

Much less effort is devoted to the air support of naval operations than those on land, reflecting the overriding Soviet preoccupation with its ground forces. However, among the important missions undertaken by the Naval Air Force are anti-submarine warfare and 'over the horizon' targeting of surface ships for anti-shipping missiles. Both land-based aircraft and shipborne helicopters are employed for these tasks and land-based bombers may themselves carry missiles. Priority targets for Soviet naval forces are enemy ballistic-missile submarines and carrier strike forces are important secondary targets. Although military supply convoys and commercial shipping (especially oil tankers) could become the targets of Soviet naval aircraft, their missions are primarily defensive. The Yak-36 Forger strike fighters carried aboard *Kiev*-class VTOL carriers have only a limited offensive capability, but the Soviet Navy's abilities in this respect could be considerably enhanced by the deployment of true aircraft carriers before the end of the century.

ABOVE: Riflemen board Mil Mi-8 troop transports in Byelorussia, 1979, before being flown to the 'enemy' rear during military exercises.

The Strategic Rocket Forces (*Raketnye voiska strategicheskogo naznacheniya*) ranks above all other Soviet armed forces in recognition of the fact that the Soviet Union's 'superpower' status is due first and foremost to its strategic nuclear capabilities.

The formation of the Strategic Rocket Forces in May 1960 followed a speech by Nikita Khrushchev to the Supreme Soviet in which he declared that henceforth no area of an enemy's territory would be immune from attack by Soviet nuclear forces during the first minutes of war. The military forces which underpinned this bellicose rhetoric were to say the least modest, comprising some 35 of the first-generation SS-6 Sapwood intercontinental ballistic missile (ICBM). The SS-6 proved to be unreliable in service, required lengthy prelaunch preparations before it could be fired and was totally unprotected against attack on its above-ground launching pad. However, the mere threat of Soviet ICBM attack on the American homeland provoked a 'missile gap' crisis in the United States during the 1960 Presidential election campaign.

Thus assured of the valuable political leverage conferred on the possessors of even a modest ICBM force, the Soviet Union pressed ahead with the development of a second generation of land-based ICBMs in the early 1960s, with the first of these (the SS-7 Saddler) entering service in 1962. Shorter-range medium and intermediate range ballistic missiles, targeted on Western Europe, were available in greater numbers. It was an attempt to emplace SS-4 Sandal IRBMs in Cuba in the fall in 1962 which revealed the true weakness of the Soviet strategic position. Khrushchev was forced to back down in the face of American pressure and withdraw the IRBMs from Cuba, but the humiliation only reinforced the Soviet belief that a strong nuclear arsenal was the only means of restraining United States aggression. Soviet ICBMs began to be emplaced in protective silos from 1964 onward and it was during the early 1960s that the first Soviet submarine-launched ballistic missile, the inaccurate and short-range (350 nautical miles) SS-N-4 Sark, was first deployed.

Khrushchev's successor Leonid Brezhnev continued to give priority to the development and deployment of Soviet ICBMs and with the appearance of the third-generation SS-9 Scarp, SS-11 Sego and SS-13 Savage in the mid 1960s the Strategic Rocket Forces began a period of dramatic expansion. The massive SS-9 was a three-stage missile propelled by liquid fuel which could be stored aboard, thus

PREVIOUS PAGES: An artist's impression of the Blackjack bomber expected to enter service later in the 1980s. Although superficially similar to the Rockwell B-1, it is in fact much larger and heavier. RIGHT: Though paraded through the Moscow streets for public inspection, the SS-10 was not, in fact, deployed operationally. BELOW: The SS-11 remains the most numerous Soviet ICBM, with over 500 believed deployed, but is being replaced by the SS-17.

Strategic Rocket Forces ICBM Deployment

Missile Field Location	Missile Type(s)
Aleysk	SS-18
Derazhnya	SS-11 and SS-19
Dombarovskiy	SS-18
Drovyanaya	SS-11
Gladkaya	SS-11
Imeni Gastello	SS-18
Kartaly	SS-18
Kostroma	SS-11 and SS-17
Kozelsk	SS-11 and SS-19
Olovyannaya	SS-11
Perm	SS-11
Pervomaysk	SS-19
Svobodnyy	SS-11
Tatishchevo	SS-19
Teykovo	SS-11
Uzhur	SS-18
Yedrovo	SS-17
Yoshkar Ola	SS-13
Zhangiz Tobe	SS-18

eliminating the time-wasting process of fueling the rocket after receiving launch instructions. With a range of some 7500 miles, the SS-9 was armed with a 25 megaton warhead (the largest ever to be operationally deployed). The smaller SS-11 was the first Soviet missile to be fitted with multiple warheads, three 300 kiloton warheads being fitted to the Mod 3 version. These warheads would fall in a predetermined pattern over a single target, rather than being directed against widely separated targets, as is possible with a true MIRV (multiple independently-targeted reentry vehicle). The majority of SS-11s carried single warheads, but the introduction of MIRVs showed that the Soviet Union was fast developing the MIRV technology first applied to the United States' Minuteman III of 1970. Further improvements in missile development were shown by the SS-13 Savage, which introduced solid fuel propellants. These were not only easier to store within the missile than liquids, but they also improved missile accuracy because of their more predictable burning characteristics. By 1970 the Strategic Rocket Forces had reached a strength of 1300 ICBMs and some 350,000 personnel. Although in terms of intercontinental-range missiles deployed the Soviet Union had the edge on the United States (SAC's ICBM force stabilized at 1054 in 1967), the American lead in MIRV technology and missile accuracy tipped the balance in the United States' favor. Nonetheless, Soviet capabilities were impressive enough to lead to increasing concern about the survivability of the USAF's land-based ICBMs during the next decade.

American strategy in the 1960s had rested on the doctrine of mutually assured destruction, which recognized that if both the United States and the Soviet Union were certain to be devastated by a nuclear war then it was clearly in the interests of both to avoid such a conflict. Soviet perceptions were somewhat different, because in the view of the Kremlin leadership it was the Strategic Rocket

Forces' readiness to fight an all-out nuclear war which was restraining American aggression and safeguarding the Soviet homeland. Consequently there was a greater readiness in the Soviet Union to 'think about the unthinkable' and develop warfighting doctrines for a nuclear war than there was in the United States where the emphasis was on deterrence. Some observers have seen the Soviet willingness to contemplate fighting a nuclear war as evidence that the Soviet leadership wants such a conflict and believes it to be winnable. This is almost certainly a misjudgment of the Soviet position, which stresses that readiness to fight at all levels of conflict is the surest guarantee of security. However, this divergence in thinking between East and West did result in quite different strategic objectives, for whereas the United States sought 'sufficiency' in nuclear weapons and delivery systems (that is a high enough level of forces to ensure catastrophic damage to the Soviet Union), the Soviet Union saw safety in superior numbers of missiles and warheads.

The divergent goals of American and Soviet strategic policy were well illustrated by the SALT I (Strategic arms limitation treaty) agreement of 1972 and its aftermath. The agreement granted the Soviet Union rough strategic parity with the United States, some 1400 land-based Soviet ICBMs being permitted while the US retained its 1054 ICBMs. The American government hoped that the Soviet Union would accept this position and not seek to improve its ICBM forces further. SALT I did not restrict Soviet development and deployment of MIRVs or other technical means of enhancing the effectiveness of its ICBMs, but the agreement did limit the deployment of ABM (anti-ballistic missile) systems. Thus the Soviet Union was encouraged to develop its missile forces to the point where they posed a credible threat to the United States' land-based ICBMs. Since the SALT I agreement did not specifically prohibit this and by restricting United States' ABM deployments it removed one of the

ABOVE: The intermediate-range SS-5 was part of the early Soviet nuclear threat, but has since been replaced by the SS-20. It carried a one megaton nuclear warhead.

49

obstacles in the way of an effective Soviet counter-force capability – albeit one of unproven effectiveness – there should have been little surprise that Soviet missile developments during the 1970s greatly increased the threat to American silo-based ICBMs.

The Soviet fourth generation ICBMs (the SS-17, SS-18 and SS-19) not only introduced 'MIRVed' warheads, but also had improved 'throw weights' (that is the missile's payload, made up of the warheads, guidance system and perhaps such penetration aids as dummy warheads to confuse ABM tracking radars). This gave the Soviet Union the option of either arming these ICBMs with a number of independently targetable warheads in the 200 to 600-kiloton yield range, or of fitting them with a single massive 20-megaton warhead. The single, high-yield warheads would be directed against such targets as 'hardened' underground command bunkers. Coupled with the introduction of MIRVs was a considerable increase in the new missiles' accuracy of delivery. The CEP (circular error probable) of a warhead delivered by a third-generation SS-9 or SS-11 was about 0.5 nautical miles, whereas the CEP for a fourth generation missile had fallen to 0.25 nautical miles or less. Even so, it is doubtful whether the Soviet Union has any great confidence in its ability to knock out the greater part of the United States' Minuteman force with its present ICBMs. However, Soviet capabilities are sufficiently impressive to cause American strategic planners serious concern. The vexed debate over the viability of the MX missile system is one result of this.

One method of increasing the survivability of fixed, land-based missiles is to mount them in 'hardened' missile silos. It is generally agreed that the Soviet Union is now ahead of the United States in such techniques. The older American ICBM silos are hardened to withstand overpressures of 1000psi, whereas the later upgraded Minuteman silos can probably withstand twice this overpressure. Soviet silos are known to exceed these tolerances. During the 1970s, as the fourth-generation ICBMs were deployed, for the most part in existing rather than newly-built silos, the hardness of these structures was considerably increased. The greatest improvements were possible for those silos housing SS-17s and SS-18s, which make use of 'cold launch' techniques. This means that the missile is ejected in a launch canister from its silo by compressed gasses before the rocket motor ignites, rather than with a 'hot launch' system in which the rocket motor ignites within the silo.

One of the most significant advantages of a 'cold launch' system is that the clearance between the missile and sides of its launch silo can be appreciably reduced. It is this saving in space which the Soviet engineers have taken advantage of in beefing-up the structure of their silos when converting them to house SS-17s and SS-18s. Another useful characteristic of 'cold launch' systems is that damage to the silo is minimized during firing and therefore it is possible to reload the silo for further use. The Soviet Strategic Rocket Forces has practiced these techniques and made provision for the supply of reserve missiles and fuel to the launch sites. It has even fitted all 'hot launch' liquid-fueled missiles with canisters which are intended to minimize damage to the silo structure during firing, so that they too may be swiftly repaired and reloaded. It will be a matter of days rather than hours before such reloads can be brought into action, but with its concern for maintaining a nuclear warfighting capability the Soviet

BELOW: A Soviet ICBM in its launch silo. Soviet 'hardening' techniques are now believed superior to those of the US in protecting the missiles within the silos from attack.

Union believes that such a reinforcement potential may nonetheless be valuable.

One advantage of ICBM reloads in Soviet eyes is that such weapons are not accountable under existing strategic arms limitation agreements. Under SALT I the Soviet Union was granted a higher ceiling on the number of ICBMs that it could deploy than was the United States, in recognition of its lagging MIRV technology. However, the SALT II agreement of 1978, while making some progress in reducing the overall number of Soviet nuclear delivery systems and imposing limits on numbers of MIRVed ICBMs, cruise-missile armed bombers, etc, failed to tackle the problem of limiting deliverable warheads. As a consequence the Soviet Union has been able to outmatch the United States in both ICBMs and in warheads. The American ICBM force comprises 1045 delivery vehicles, the reduction from the long-standing total of 1054 being due to the phaseout of the Titan II which is currently in progress. These missiles carry 2145 warheads. The Soviet missile force currently includes 1398 ICBMs armed with a total of 5654 warheads. This comparison ignores submarine-launched ballistic missiles and in fact here the United States has the edge over the Soviet Union.

A grand total of 5152 warheads arm the 568 American SLBMs, while the Soviet Navy has only 2688 warheads carried by 980 missiles. However, in the American view these weapons represent a secure second strike force and so they will not be targeted on Soviet strategic forces. It seems that the Soviet long-range SLBMs are regarded in the same manner as survivable nuclear forces, which can be used to threaten enemy cities after the initial nuclear exchanges directed against nuclear delivery systems and their control networks. However, shorter-range Soviet SLBMs are believed to be targeted on American strategic forces, most notably Strategic Air Command (SAC) bomber airfields. These are large and unprotected targets which can be easily destroyed by a SLBM-delivered warhead, unlike missile silos which require a greater accuracy than that at present available from SLBMs. SAC's manned bomber force too greatly outnumbers its Soviet equivalent in intercontinental range aircraft. However, it is entirely characteristic of Soviet military thinking that, instead of attempting to match the United States' balanced strategic nuclear forces, they have rather concentrated on developing an immensely powerful armory of land-based ICBMs. These weapons have the very characteristics of speed, range and destructive power so beloved of Soviet military theory.

The Strategic Rocket Forces at present has a manpower strength of 325,000 and its 1398 ICBMs are organized within six operational rocket armies. Each missile launcher constitutes a battery and these are assigned to battalions and regiments. The present missile force is a mixture of third and fourth-generation weapons. The most numerous ICBM type remains the SS-11 Sego, with 550 deployed in missile fields at Derazhnya, Kozelsk, Teykovo, Kostroma, Perm, Gladkaya, Drovyanaya, Olovyannaya and Svobodnyy. A single field of 60 SS-13 Savage missiles is at Yoshkar Ola. There are 150 SS-17s deployed in two fields at Kostroma (alongside SS-11s) and at Yedrovo. The SS-18 fields are at Dombarovskiy, Kartaly, Imeni Gastello, Aleysk, Zhangiz Tobe and Uzhur, with a total of 308 missiles of this type deployed. Most widely used of the fourth-generation ICBMs is the SS-19, 330 of which

are distributed between missile fields at Derazhnya, Kozelsk, Pervomaysk and Tatishchevo. In addition to these operational sites, Strategic Rocket Forces control three missile test centers, the most important of which is the Tyuratam missile and space center. There are some 300 launch control centers housed in hardened underground bunkers and these are backed up by airborne command posts.

The SS-17 missile, which is believed to have the Soviet designation RS-16, is in the same class as the earlier SS-11 which it has partially replaced. However, it has a much greater throw-weight than the earlier missile. Three versions are reported to be in service, two of which (the Mod 1 and Mod 3

ABOVE: The three-warhead SS-20 has replaced the earlier SS-4 and 5 missiles, thereby greatly increasing Soviet theater nuclear strike capability.

BELOW: Few examples of the SS-13 exist, a single field of 60 being the extent of its deployment in the mid 1980s.

ABOVE: Seen but rarely on land, the SS-N-6 ballistic missile is sub-launched. Some 16 are deployed on each *Yankee*-class Soviet submarine.
RIGHT: The ABM-1 Galosh is the world's only anti-ballistic missile currently operational. 32 such missiles are sited around Moscow.

variants) are fitted with four independently-targetable warheads. It is believed that the difference between them is in warhead yield, one carrying 200-kiloton warheads and the other 600 kiloton warheads. The third version carries a single high-yield warhead and this, combined with the missile's high accuracy, makes it an ideal weapon for use against hardened missile silos and command bunkers. Range is some 6200 miles for the MIRVed versions, while the single-warhead Mod 2's range is 600 miles greater. Launch weight of the SS-17 is some 143,000lb while the SS-19 (Soviet designation RS-18) is rather heavier at a launch weight of 172,000lb. However, the two missiles are in much the same class and they may well have been developed in parallel as an insurance against the failure of one of them. Unlike the SS-17, the SS-19 is hot launched rather than cold launched but in other respects it is a more advanced weapon and twice as

many SS-19s have been deployed. There are three versions in service, the Mod 1 and Mod 3 having six independently targetable warheads while the Mod 2 has a single warhead. The range of the Mod 2 and Mod 3 versions is 6200 miles, while the Mod 1's is 250 miles less.

The SS-18 (Soviet designation RS-20) is a real heavyweight among Soviet strategic missiles, with a launch weight of some 485,000lb. This is even greater than the 420,000lb launch weight of the superseded SS-9 and the SS-18 has a 30 percent greater throw-weight than the earlier missile. This is reflected in the diversity and capability of the warhead loads in the four versions of the missile which have been deployed since 1974. The basic missile is a two-stage, liquid fueled vehicle which makes use of cold launch techniques. In its Mod 1 version it carries a single high yield warhead of 24 megatons over a range of 7400 miles, while CEP is reported to

ABOVE: Currently in the experimental stage, the SS-X-25 is a small single-warhead missile based on mobile launchers such as the one depicted emerging bottom left.

be about 1300ft. The Mod 2 carries a MIRVed payload, which can be made up of between eight and ten warheads with yields ranging from 550 to 900 kilotons. CEP is similar to that of the Mod 1, while range at 6800 miles is appreciably less. Mod 3 like Mod 1 carries a single warhead (of 20 megaton yield), but has a considerably improved range of 10,000 miles. Accuracy has also improved with this model and CEP is down to 1150ft. Mod 4 is armed with ten 500 kiloton yield warheads, plus four decoys, and can deliver these to within a CEP of as little as 820ft.

Two new Soviet solid-propellant fueled missiles

are currently under development. One of these, identified as the SS-X-24, is in the same size and weight class as the United States' MX. It is likely to be based in superhardened silos and its MIRVed warheads are expected to have a CEP of less than 800ft. The second new ICBM, the SS-X-25, is a small single-warhead missile which is to be based on mobile launchers similar to those used by the SS-20 intermediate-range ballistic missile. Like the United States, the Soviet Union appears to be worried that large, silo-based ICBMs – especially those with a large number of independently targeted warheads – will in future become too vulnerable to

and SS-X-25, both of which have been test-launched, liquid-fueled replacements for the SS-18 and SS-17/19 are also being developed.

Soviet work on a new generation of ICBMs has led to a number of accusations from United States senators that the SALT II agreements are being violated. Although SALT II was never ratified by the United States legislature, in reprisal for the Soviet invasion of Afghanistan, both sides nonetheless have reached tacit agreement to be bound by its provisions. One point of issue is that by developing more than one system the Soviet Union has broken the agreement which permits the development, test and deployment of only one new ICBM by each of the signatory powers. However, there seems to be sufficient diplomatic ambiguity written into this provision to justify development work on several new ICBM systems. Less justifiable are Soviet attempts to deny the United States intelligence information on the performance of these systems under test by encrypting the telemetry transmitted to ground stations. SALT II specifically states that 'neither party shall engage in deliberate denial of telemetric information, such as through use of telemetric encryption, whenever such denial impedes verification of compliance with the provisions of the Treaty.' Clearly Soviet concern with security and deception outweighs any consideration of confidence-building between potential adversaries.

Although the primary responsibility of Strategic Rocket Forces is for the Soviet ICBM force, the service also controls the medium and intermediate range ballistic missiles which carry out theater nuclear strike missions. There are about 600 of these missiles in service, two thirds of them deployed in the western military districts of the Soviet Union, with the remainder in the central and Far Eastern districts. The replacement of the older SS-4 Sandal and SS-5 Skean missiles with the SS-20 has greatly increased Soviet theater nuclear strike capabilities. This is due in part to the increase in deliverable warheads, as each SS-20 is fitted with three independently-targetable reentry vehicles. Consequently, even though the overall number of launch vehicles has decreased since the late 1970s the number of warheads in service has more than

BELOW: The vehicle-launched SS-20 can reach targets throughout the NATO rear areas in Europe with its 3100-mile range. The launch vehicle may be reloaded for further firings, and the system represents a significant new threat to the West.

counterforce action. The answer to the problem can either be to emplace such missiles in superhardened silos, or to switch to mobile ICBMs, which offer both a more elusive target than a fixed missile and a less attractive one because only one warhead is carried. Recent tests conducted in the United States – as a direct result of the USAF Foreign Technology Division's investigations of Soviet practice – have suggested that silos can be constructed to withstand overpressures of as much as 50,000psi. It appears that the Soviet Union is actively developing both mobile and superhardened basing systems for its fifth generation of ICBMs. In addition to the SS-X-24

doubled. Furthermore, as each SS-20's mobile launcher can immediately be fitted with a reload missile after firing, a sustained nuclear strike against enemy rear areas can be planned. Other notable improvements in Soviet capabilities with the deployment of the SS-20 include a greater accuracy of delivery and a faster reaction time. As the SS-20 is fired from a mobile launcher, it is less vulnerable to enemy preemptive action than the fixed sites of the earlier missiles. Finally, in comparison with the SS-4 (1250 mile range) the SS-20 (3100 mile range) can reach targets throughout the NATO rear areas in Europe and is even able to cover the defense installations on Greenland. Soviet SS-20 deployments also threaten the greater part of North Africa, the Middle East and the Asian landmass. The 360 SS-20s in service at the end of 1983 were divided between the Western Soviet Union (162 missiles), Central Asia (90 missiles) and the Far East (108 missiles). The remaining SS-4s (223 missiles) and SS-5s (16 missiles) are being progressively withdrawn as the newer missiles enter service.

Quite apart from the desirability of improving and updating the medium and intermediate range missile force, the widespread availability of the SS-20 has freed a sizeable number of medium-range bombers and interdiction aircraft for the conventional attack mission. From the early 1980s all these aircraft, together with the small Soviet long-range strategic bomber force, have been grouped together in the Aviation Armies of the Soviet Union (AASU). The new Air Force command is formed from the forces of the now-defunct Long Range

Aviation and the Su-24 Fencer-equipped interdiction regiments, which were formerly part of Frontal Aviation. AASU is organized into numbered air armies, as used to be the case with Frontal Aviation, and it controls over 1100 combat aircraft and 100,000 military personnel. The five air armies comprise: 24th Air Army with headquarters at Leignica in Poland, equipped with Su-24 Fencers; 4th Air Army with headquarters at Venitza equipped with Su-24 Fencers; 30th Air Army with headquarters at Irkutsk equipped with Tu-16 Badgers, Tu-26 Backfires and Su-24 Fencers; 46th Air Army with headquarters at Smolensk equipped with Tu-16 Badgers, Tu-22 Blinders and Tu-26 Backfires; and 36th Air Army with headquarters at Moscow equipped with Mya-4 Bisons, Tu-16 Badgers and Tu-20 Bears. The 24th and 4th Air Armies carry out interdiction and, if necessary, tactical nuclear strike in support of the Central Europe and South-Western Europe theaters of military operations. The 30th Air Army will perform interdiction and theater strategic missions in the Far East theater of military operations, while the 46th Air Army is responsible for the latter mission in the European TVDs. Finally the 36th Air Army will carry out the intercontinental-range strategic nuclear mission. The greater part of the AASU's forces, some 500 aircraft in total, are concentrated in the Western Soviet Union and Eastern Europe.

By far the weakest element of the AASU, both in terms of numbers deployed and in capability, is the long-range bomber force. This comprises 100 turbo-prop-powered Tu-20 Bear and 43 Mya-4 Bison

BELOW: A Myasishchev Mya-4, codenamed Bison by NATO, is escorted by a US Navy Phantom over the Mediterranean, 1964.

bombers, some fitted with air-to-surface missiles to give a stand-off attack capability. The long awaited rejuvenation of the force is now in prospect, with the Blackjack variable-geometry-wing strategic bomber expected to enter service in 1986-7. Virtually all strategic targets within the United States are within range of the Soviet long-range bombers and their mission radius can be extended either by making use of in-flight refueling (although not all the bombers are equipped for this and the tanker force is at any rate a small one) or by staging through advanced air bases in the Soviet Arctic. The capabilities of the Tu-26 Backfire have been a matter for debate. The United States wished to class the aircraft as a long-range bomber during the SALT II negotiations, but this was firmly rebutted by the Soviet negotiators who insisted that it was a medium-range bomber. Certainly the Soviet deployments of Backfire with the Air Armies committed to theater nuclear strike rather than with the intercontinental-range bombers of 36th Air Army would seem to bear this out. However, there can be no doubt that the high performance Backfire could cover most of the United States if it staged through the Arctic bases and was refueled in flight. SALT II has resulted in the removal of flight refueling probes from the aircraft as a confidence-building measure intended to reassure the Americans that Backfire poses no threat to the United States. This is an empty gesture since, as the internal 'plumbing' required for in-flight refueling presumably remains fitted, it will only take a matter of hours to replace the probes. Backfire will certainly stand a much better chance of evading NORAD's air defenses than will the elderly Bear and Bison bombers. Yet in view of the emphasis that Soviet doctrine places on a swift conventional victory and the concentration of strategic nuclear forces within the Strategic

Rocket Forces (rather than a balanced distribution between air, land-based and sea-based systems), it is likely that Backfire is primarily a theater rather than an intercontinental strike aircraft.

The Tu-20 Bear first entered Soviet Air Force service in 1956 and has been built in six major variants. In 1983 the type was put back into production in order to provide an additional launch platform for the AS-X-15 long-range cruise missile. Incidentally, the designation Tu-95 for the Bear, widely used since its appearance in the SALT II document in this form, is almost certainly the design bureau's project number and not the Soviet Air Force's designation. It is unlikely that any military organization would designate successive items of equipment in the sequence Tu-16, Tu-95, Tu-22. The Tu-20 owes its longevity primarily to its out-

TOP: Despite its swept tail surfaces, the Tu-20's rear fuselage betrays its World War II origins in the Boeing B-29.

ABOVE: With a fuselage length of 155ft and wingspan of 167ft, the Tu-20 remains one of the Soviet Union's larger bomber/ reconnaissance types. The wing is full of fuel, contributing to the type's great range.

RIGHT: A cutaway
drawing of a Tupolev
Tu-16 Badger bomber
showing internal detail.
BELOW RIGHT: A more
recent development
from the Tupolev design
bureau, the Tu-26
Backfire caused alarm in
NATO circles on its
introduction in the
1970s due to its
perceived strategic
applications.

standing range characteristics, which have been
largely achieved by filling the entire internal volume
of the 167ft 8in-span swept wing with fuel. The four
massive 15,000shp Kuznetsov NK-12 turboprops
also contribute to the Tu-20's range (11,000 miles
maximum, extensible by in-flight refueling)
through their economical fuel consumption. However, they have the drawback of limiting performance to a maximum speed of 540mph. This is clearly
inadequate when matched against the 1500mph
performance of even the elderly F-106 interceptors
serving with the USAF. Furthermore the Tu-20's
large wing will be subjected to considerable buffet-
ing during low level flight and so this means of
evading early radar detection cannot be exploited to
the full. A further complication is the Tu-20's
conspicuous radar 'signature'; partly a result of the
bomber's large size, but more especially due to its
four pairs of 18ft 5in diameter counter-rotating
propellers which act as highly-effective radar re-
flectors. As the USAF air defense forces' latest
modernization plans are fully implemented, with
detection and engagement of targets at all altitudes
made possible through the combination of E-3A
AWACS airborne radar aircraft and F-15 Eagle
interceptors with a 'lookdown/shootdown' capability, the prospects for a successful Soviet penetration
of American airspace appear to diminish yet further.

In one respect the Myasishchev Mya-4 Bison is
better suited to the strategic bomber mission than its
near contemporary the Tu-20, as it is a turbojet-
powered aircraft capable of a high subsonic performance (680mph or Mach 0.95 at 10,000ft).
However, even this improvement is clearly insuffi-

cient to counter the speed advantage of its likely
adversaries. Yet in order to improve its speed performance, the Mya-4 has had to sacrifice some of the
range which is the Tu-20's most outstanding attri-
bute. The Mya-4's four 28,600lb thrust Soloviev
D-15 turbojets are both high on fuel consumption
and relatively inefficient at low altitudes. This
results in a range of some 7000 miles, carrying a
10,000lb payload. Range can be extended by in-
flight refueling, but another means of extending a
bomber's radius of action – the fitting of air-to-
surface stand-off missiles – has been ruled out by the
Bison's undercarriage design. This makes use of
twin-bogie main units mounted on the fuselage
centerline, with outrigger wheels beneath the wing-
tips. As a consequence there is insufficient ground
clearance to permit an externally-mounted ASM to

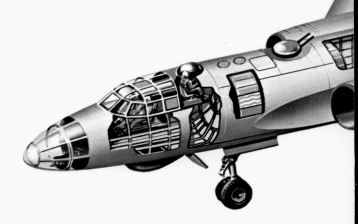

BELOW: Backfire in
flight, with the
underfuselage AS-4
Kitchen missile clearly
visible in this view.

be carried. Both the Mya-4 and the Tu-20 carry a defensive armament of paired 23mm cannon, mounted in dorsal and ventral remotely-controlled barbettes and in a manned tail position.

The standard ASM fitted to the strategic bomber variants of the Bear is the AS-3 Kangaroo and the AS-4 Kitchen may also be carried. The former, which first appeared in the early 1960s, is a large supersonic cruise missile. Its configuration is that of a swept-wing fighter aircraft, with a launch weight of some 22,000lb. After release from the parent aircraft it flies at a speed of around Mach 1.6 under radio command guidance for the initial portion of its mission. Thereafter an autopilot takes over to complete the guidance to a target 400 miles from the launching point. This system is both highly in-

accurate and vulnerable to interception by fighter aircraft. However, it can probably deliver a thermonuclear warhead against such large targets as industrial centers and ports with sufficient accuracy to ensure their destruction. Although some sources claim that a 5000lb high explosive warhead can also be fitted to the AS-3, it is difficult to imagine what military targets could be realistically attacked by such an inaccurate weapon. The AS-4 is a rocket powered, Mach 2.5 ASM, which is usually fitted to the Tu-22 Blinder and Tu-26 Backfire but may also be carried by the Tu-20. It makes use of an inertial guidance system and its range is 400 miles when launched at low altitude or double this when launched at high altitude.

Even when making allowance for the effectiveness of stand-off weapon delivery and the possible effectiveness of defensive armament and ECM jamming and deception, the chances of a Soviet long-range bomber penetrating NORAD's air defense system appear to be remote. Of course, if strategic targets in the People's Republic of China are attacked the odds become rather better, with bombers of the mid 1950s being countered by interceptors and radar systems of much the same vintage. However, it should be realized that the Soviet bombers will not have to run the gauntlet of a fully-effective air defense system when attacking the United States. This is because in the event of a nuclear war the first wave of attacks will come from land and sea-based ballistic missiles with flight times of 30 minutes and less. Therefore, the bombers (after a flight of perhaps eight hours) will be making follow-up attacks on American strategic forces which have already been

Aircraft Strength of Aviation Armies of the Soviet Union		
Type	**Role**	**No:**
Tu-20 Bear	LR Bomber	100
Mya-4 Bison	LR Bomber	70
Tu-16 Badger	MR Bomber	220
Tu-22 Blinder	MR Bomber	125
Tu-26 Backfire	MR Bomber	110
Su-24 Fencer	Interdiction	550
Tu-20 Bear	Recce/ELINT	4
Tu-16 Badger	Recce/ELINT	15
Tu-22 Blinder	Recce/ELINT	15
Tu-16 Badger	ECM	90
Mya-4 Bison	Tanker	30
Tu-16 Badger	Tanker	18

severely degraded by nuclear attack. Of course the priority target for a Soviet first strike against the United States will be nuclear delivery systems and their command and control networks. Yet even when due allowance is made for their coverage, the Soviet missile forces will have sufficient warheads remaining to cover such fixed (and therefore vulnerable) elements of the NORAD air defense system as ground radars, command centers and interceptor airfields. Consequently there may be little effective and coordinated opposition to the Soviet bombers.

The long-overdue replacement of the Tu-20 Bear and Mya-4 Bison after more than thirty years' front-line service with the Soviet Air Force will have to await the introduction into service of the Tupolev Blackjack later in the decade. Blackjack is a four-engined variable-geometry-wing bomber, superficially similar in appearance to the American Rockwell B-1. However, with an estimated maximum take-off weight of 580,000lb compared with the B-1B's 390,000lb, it is a considerably larger and heavier aircraft. Indeed it is larger even than the USAF's massive B-52 Stratofortress. Its variable sweep wings give Blackjack a combination of good take-off and cruising flight characteristics with the wing fully spread, combined with a high speed dash performance and improved handling and gust-reponse at low level for target penetration. The bomber's maximum speed at high altitude is estimated at Mach 2.3.

A combat radius without in-flight refueling at 4500 miles is sufficient to cover any target within the United States, or the greater part of the Asian landmass. By the time that Blackjack is in widespread service in the early 1990s, the Soviet Air Force will have acquired a long-range air launched cruise missile of similar size and performance to the

USAF's AGM-86B. This is the 1600-mile range AS-X-15, which is currently at an advanced stage of its development. Presumably Blackjack will be fitted with a combination of such weapons and free-fall nuclear bombs.

The most effective of the Soviet medium-range bombers assigned to the theater nuclear strike and deep interdiction missions is the Tu-26 Backfire. As with the Tu-20 Bear some confusion has arisen as to this bomber's true designation. In the SALT II documents it is designated Tu-22M, suggesting a development of the Tu-22 Blinder. However, since the Backfire design quite obviously owes nothing to the earlier aircraft and as it was clearly to the Soviet SALT negotiators' advantage to confuse the issue by

ABOVE: Mechanics service the two rear-mounted afterburning turbojets of a Tu-22 Blinder. Top speed of the type is Mach 1.5.
BELOW: With its distinctively bulged radar nose, Blinder-B usually carries an AS-4 Kitchen stand-off missile, but this has yet to be fitted to the example seen awaiting operations here.

RIGHT: Sukhoi's variable geometry Su-24 Fencer is depicted with its wing in a forward-swept position for take-off or landing. High-speed or cruising flight requires a greater degree of sweep.

ABOVE: F-4 Phantom confronts Tu-16 Badger in international airspace. Like the turboprop Tu-20 Bear, the Badger has latterly been pressed into service as an ECM and reconnaissance type.

suggesting Backfire's affinity with a bomber which indisputably lacked intercontinental range, I have treated the Tu-22M designation as fallacious. Implicit in the debate over Backfire's intercontinental capabilities is the recognition that it possesses outstandingly good payload/range characteristics for a medium bomber. As with the Blackjack, a combination of economical cruising flight with supersonic dash capabilities has been obtained by using a variable-geometry wing. With an unrefueled combat radius of 3400 miles, Backfire can reach targets anywhere in Western Europe or in the People's Republic of China. It can also cover much of the Northern Atlantic and Western Pacific and for this reason Backfire's production has been equally distributed between AASU and the Naval Air Force, each command having about 100 Tu-26s on strength. This deployment incidentally is a further confirmation that Backfire is in Soviet eyes a medium bomber, because if it were an intercontinental range strategic weapon AASU would undoubtedly have been given priority over the Naval Air Force in reequipment.

The Tu-26 is powered by a pair of Kuznetsov NK-144 turbofans, which each develop some 45,000lb with afterburning. This gives the bomber a maximum speed of Mach 2 at altitudes of 40,000ft and above, reducing to high subsonic speed (about Mach 0.9) at low levels. The Tu-26's nose-mounted Down Beat attack and navigation radar may also be used for terrain avoidance during target penetration runs at low level. A conventional weapons load of up to 17,500lb of bombs can be carried on external hardpoints beneath the engine intakes and in an internal weapons bay. For stand-off attack an AS-4 Kitchen missile can be fitted in a semi-recessed mounting within the weapons bay. The 430-mile-range AS-6 Kingfish ASM has also been reported to be carried by the Backfire. This is a rocket-powered missile with inertial guidance and terminal homing by radar. As such it is particularly effective against shipping targets, which provide good radar returns, and significantly AASU has a secondary maritime attack mission in support of the Naval Air Force.

Backfire's main defenses against interception are the tactical expedients of evasive routing to avoid highly defended areas, the use of stand-off weapons and low-level target penetration. However, the bomber also carries a defensive armament of twin 23mm cannon mounted in a remotely-operated and

radar-directed tail turret. It is also certainly equipped with ECM equipment and one of its four crewmembers may be an electronic warfare officer.

The two other medium bombers assigned to
AASU are the Tu-22 Blinder and Tu-16 Badger.
Surprisingly enough, although the Badger is a
decade older than the Tu-22, it serves in greater
numbers, not only in the bomber role (220 currently
in use) but also as a reconnaissance, ECM and
tanker aircraft. The Badger, which first flew in
1952, is certainly now showing its age and 90 of the
type have recently been retired from the bombing
role. Nonetheless, this robust and uncomplicated
design has demonstrated a versatility that the more
specialized Tu-22 lacks. The Blinder's greatest
operational shortcoming is its lack of range and for
this reason it was only produced in limited numbers,
some 125 remaining in service as bombers. It was
originally conceived as a medium level bomber,
which would be able to use its supersonic dash
(Mach 1.5) capability to evade interception over
the target area. However, by the time that it entered
service in the early 1960s, Western air defenses were
sufficiently far advanced to be able to counter the
Blinder's penetration tactics. As a result its main
operational role has been as a stand-off bomber,
armed with the AS-4 Kitchen ASM.

The Tu-22 is powered by two 30,000lb thrust
afterburning turbojets, which are housed in distinctive tail-mounted nacelles. Its streamlined shape,
with dramatically swept wings and area-ruled fuselage, give the aircraft a predatory appearance which
is belied by its disappointing combat capabilities.
Nonetheless, it introduced such innovations on
Soviet bombers as a powerful nose-mounted
nav/attack radar and radar-directed tail armament
(twin 23mm cannon). It can carry a warload of
17,500lb in two internal weapons bays over a typical

ABOVE: One of the first
color pictures ever taken
of the Su-24 Fencer,
taken over the Baltic
Sea in 1985 by a Swedish
Air Force fighter.

Aviation Armies of the Soviet Union	
AASU Headquarters	Moscow
4th Air Army Su-24 Fencer	Venitza
24th Air Army Su-24 Fencer	Leignica, Poland
30th Air Army Tu-16 Badger, Tu-26 Backfire, Su-24 Fencer	Irkutsk
46th Air Army Tu-16 Badger, Tu-22 Blinder, Tu-26 Backfire	Smolensk
36th Air Army Tu-16 Badger, Tu-20 Bear, Mya-4 Bison	Moscow

ABOVE: Close-up of the forward fuselage of a Tupolev Tu-16 Badger cruising over the North Atlantic. Broadly comparable to the Vickers Valiant, now long withdrawn from RAF service, the Soviet type soldiers on in the mid 1980s.

mission radius of 1750 miles. It is ironical that the Blinder, envisioned as a supersonic successor to the Badger, has proved to be one of the least flexible Soviet bomber aircraft.

The swept-wing Tu-16 Badger is powered by two powerful (by the standards of the 1950s) 19,200lb thrust Mikulin AM-3 turbojets, which give it a range of 4000 miles and a maximum speed of Mach 0.9. Up to 13,000lb of ordnance can be carried internally in the weapons bay and the defensive armament comprises seven 23mm cannon. Missile armament, carried underwing, comprises either a pair of AS-5 Kelt missiles or a single AS-6 Kingfish. The AS-5 is a subsonic rocket-powered missile with a maximum range of 200 miles. Guidance is by means of an autopilot with radar terminal homing and the warhead is 2200lb of conventional high explosive. The Tu-16/AS-5 combination was used in action by Egypt against Israel during the Yom Kippur War of 1973, when 20 of the 25 missiles fired were shot down by interceptors or surface-to-air missiles. Thus the effectiveness of the Tu-16 against modern defenses is somewhat dubious, although in the AS-6 Kingfish ASM it has a faster and longer-ranging missile armament than with the AS-5.

A wide range of strategic support roles are carried out by modified Tu-16s, with specialized in-flight refueling tanker, electronic warfare and reconnaissance versions in service. Most numerous of these are the 90 Badger-H and -J EW aircraft, the former

equipped primarily as a chaff dispenser while the Badger-J carries ECM jamming transmitters. Their role is to blind enemy radars so that the bomber aircraft can penetrate a defended zone without being detected. Eighteen Badgers serve in the tanker role, with a refueling hose-and-drogue unit mounted in the weapons bay or fitted with a unique wingtip-to-wingtip system for refueling other Badgers. Unlike the USAF with its massive fleet of over 600 tanker aircraft, the Soviet Air Force has only a modest in-flight refueling capability.

In addition to these there are 30 Mya-4 Bison-B tankers in service. The smallness of this force reflects both the relatively low priority accorded to the intercontinental-range bombing mission by the Soviet Air Force and the availability of numerous airfields within the Soviet Union for the movement of tactical aircraft. A Soviet fighter regiment can redeploy from Eastern Europe to the Far East theater by staging through Soviet airfields each within easy range of the next, whereas an American tactical fighter wing moving from Europe to the Pacific theater must make long overwater flights for which tanker support is essential. A tanker conversion of the Ilyushin Il-76 Candid transport aircraft has for several years been reported to be under development, but it has yet to be operationally deployed. If it should be produced in considerable numbers and Soviet tactical fighters equipped for in-flight refueling, then the Soviet Air Force will thereby have greatly increased their tactical flexibility. However, there appears to be little urgency accorded to the Il-76 tanker's development and its slow progress from testing to deployment is unlikely to be totally attributable to technical difficulties.

Strategic reconnaissance is undertaken by a force of 34 aircraft variously equipped with visual and electronic intelligence-gathering sensors. ELINT (electronic intelligence) is the primary mission of 15 Tu-16 Badger-D, -E, -F and -K variants and a similar number of Blinder-Cs offer a supersonic capability at altitude. Four of the massive Tu-20s have been equipped for ELINT and visual reconnaissance as Bear-Es, their 22,000lb payload enabling them to carry a more comprehensive range of sensors than the medium bomber conversions. Since the retirement of the Yak-25RD Mandrake in the 1970s, the Soviet Air Force has lacked a high-altitude strategic reconnaissance capability. This may be due in part to the widespread use of reconnaissance satellites and also to the high capabilities of Frontal Aviation's MiG-25 Foxbat-B and D tactical reconnaissance aircraft. However, a belated successor to the Mandrake, designated Ram-M by the United States Defense Intelligence Agency, is currently being tested. Normally a NATO reporting name (eg Backfire, Foxbat) is not allocated to a Soviet aircraft until it enters series production. The Ram designation followed by a suffix letter is an interim reporting name for prototypes photographed by reconsats at the Soviet Air Force's air test center at Ramenskoye 25 miles southeast of Moscow. Ram-M is in much the same class as the USAF's Lockheed U-2, except that it has a twin tail unit rather than a single fin and rudder. Clearly reconnaissance satellites do not offer a complete coverage of Soviet intelligence targets and, like the USAF, the Soviet Air Force considers a manned strategic reconnaissance aircraft to offer greater operational flexibility.

If little is known about the latest Soviet strategic reconnaissance aircraft, there is even less information on airborne command posts. However, it is known that they are in service and during 1983 Warsaw Pact exercises practiced communication

BELOW: A Badger-D is pictured on an electronic reconnaissance mission north of the British Isles.

between these aircraft at the national command and tactical levels. Tactical airborne command is exercised from such aircraft as the An-12 Cub transport and Mil Mi-8 Hip helicopters. Yet is is likely that a more modern transport aircraft than the Cub is used for command and control at national level. Possible candidates for this mission are the Il-86 wide-bodied airliner or the Il-76 military transport. As well as communicating with Strategic Rocket Forces launch control headquarters, of which there are about 300, the national command post aircraft can also contact ballistic missile submarines. This implies that the Naval Air Force has a communica-

tions relay aircraft similar to the US Navy's TACAMO Hercules and this may well be its Soviet equivalent the An-12 Cub, or perhaps a modified Tu-20 Bear.

In contrast to the USAF, which assigns its F-111 interdiction/tactical nuclear strike aircraft to Tactical Air Command rather than to Strategic Air Command, the Soviet Air Force has grouped its Su-24 Fencers within AASU. Indeed the recognition that the Fencer had given the Soviet armed forces a hitherto-unattainable capability to carry out precision air strikes deep in enemy territory was most probably a major factor in the decision to create the

Aviation Armies of the Soviet Union as a major new command. At the time when the Fencer first entered service in the late 1970s it was assigned to Frontal Aviation's air armies, with the 37th Air Army in Poland receiving priority in supply. However, as the number of Fencers in service increased (with a total of 600 anticipated in front-line regiments by 1984), a more rational command arrangement was needed. As a result, the Fencer units were reassigned to the new AASU command alongside such theater strategic bombers as the Tu-26. Hitherto, there had been a fairly clear dividing line between the roles of such battlefield interdiction aircraft as the Yak-28 Brewer and the theater strategic Tu-16 and Tu-22. The former could penetrate the enemy's rear areas to a depth of some 270 nautical miles, carrying a fairly small bombload of 3600lb, and deliver it against pinpoint targets while flying at low level to escape interception. The medium bombers were able to range far more deeply, but lacked the capability to find and attack small targets with conventional ordnance and so used nuclear stand-off weapons against large fixed targets. The introduction of the Tu-26 allowed the Soviet Air Force to attack theater strategic targets precisely with conventional ordnance, while the Fencer could attack interdiction targets throughout the enemy rear. In a war in Europe the Fencer can cover NATO rear area targets in eastern Britain and eastern France, whereas its predecessor the Brewer was restricted to West Germany and the eastern Netherlands.

Soviet interdiction targets will certainly include nuclear warheads and their delivery systems. For example USAF Europe's F-111 bases at Lakenheath and Upper Heyford in the United Kingdom are both within range of the Fencer. Enemy headquarters and their communications equipment will also come under attack, as will air defense radars. Airfield attacks will be directed at runways, parked aircraft or their hardened shelters and stocks of fuel and ammunition in order to neutralize the enemy's tactical air force. In an offensive against NATO forces the airfields and ports used for transatlantic reinforcement, together with stockpiled equipment, will be interdiction targets. Other possible target systems are such communications choke points as road and rail junctions and bridges, industrial complexes, or army garrisons. Clearly interdiction target planners are faced with an *embarras de richesse* and will not be able to cover all possible targets adequately. Soviet priorities may correspond with the order of this listing. In any case some objectives will be allocated to army raiding forces and possibly to tactical missiles. The Soviet Union is unlikely to use nuclear warheads at the outset, but may well employ chemical weapons.

The salient characteristics of the Su-24 Fencer are its range, its ability to fly fast and low following the contours of the ground to evade air defenses and its capability to navigate, find and attack targets in all weathers. It is a two-seat variable-geometry-wing aircraft, similar in configuration to the USAF's F-111 aircraft although it is both smaller and lighter. It is powered by two turbofans which develop about 19,500lb of thrust each with afterburning, giving the Fencer a maximum speed of Mach 2 at 36,000ft and Mach 1.2 at low level. It is armed with a twin-barrel 23mm cannon and can carry up to 12,500lb of ordnance, including laser-guided bombs and the six-mile-range AS-7 Kerry air-to-surface missile.

The offensive power concentrated within the Strategic Rocket Forces and the Aviation Armies of the Soviet Union is immense both in terms of its absolute destructiveness and in the range of targets that can be eliminated. The capabilities of these strategic and theater nuclear forces, together with SSBNs of the Soviet Navy, demonstrate that the Soviet Union's oft-declared readiness to fight at any level of conflict is not mere bombast, but is founded on a carefully nurtured military capability. It is only through such readiness, Soviet military doctrine teaches, that the safety of the homeland can truly be guaranteed.

BELOW LEFT: The wide-bodied Ilyushin Il-86 can perform not only as a troop transport – as can all Aeroflot aircraft – but may also in the future form the basis for a command and control aircraft for airborne co-ordination of Warsaw Pact forces.

The strategic air and space defense forces of the *Voyska PVO* (*Protivovozdushnaya oborona* or Troops of the Air Defense Forces) constitute the most powerful organization of their kind in the world. They comprise a vast network of air defense and ballistic missile warning radars, control centers, interceptors, surface-to-air missiles (SAMs) and the only operational anti-ballistic missile (ABM) system. The service, which ranks third in precedence below the Strategic Rocket Forces and Army, is manned by 500,000 personnel and in addition controls the air defense troops serving with the Soviet armies. This extensive and elaborate air defense system contrasts sharply with that of the United States, which deploys only 260 interceptors to the Soviet Union's 2250 and no SAMs at all compared with the Soviet inventory of some 10,000. The reasons for this disparity are in part the obsessive Soviet concern for military security (highlighted by the Korean Airlines Boeing 747 incident of 1983), but also the very real threat to Soviet targets posed by the USAF's manned bomber force and its planned extensive deployment of cruise missiles. Furthermore, not only does the Soviet Air Defense Forces have a far greater total land area to cover than does the United States air defenses, but it is vulnerable to air attack from many directions around its extensive frontiers. Commander of *Voyska* PVO is Marshal of Aviation A I Koldunov.

Like Frontal Aviation and the manned bomber force, the Air Defense Forces have been reorganized in the early 1980s in order to improve their readiness for war. In place of 16 air defense regional commands, covering the entire Soviet Union and the territories of the other six member states of the Warsaw Pact, the Air Defense Forces' command structure has been integrated with that of the tactical air and land forces. Thus the five main theaters of military operation – Central Europe, Southwest Europe, Northern Europe, South and Far East – each represent an air defense area. Command of the Troops of the Air Defense (*Voyska* PVO) within the theater is exercised by an officer who is subordinated to the overall TVD commander and acts as his adviser for air defense matters. The tactical fighter forces of Frontal Aviation assigned to the theater are integrated within the TVD command in the same manner and if necessary can be called upon to augment the Air Defense Forces' interceptors. One advantage of the new command arrangements is that air defense of Soviet territory and the air defense of Soviet military forces in the field are now treated as part of the same overall operation, rather than being compartmentalized, as they were previously. The requirements of operational efficiency have thus taken precedence over the needs of administrative convenience. Nonetheless, the five large air defense regions, while perfectly manageable commands from the point of view of operational control, are too large and unwieldy as administrative units. For this reason, the air defense forces within the 16 Military Districts come under the district's deputy commander for air defense for such nonoperational matters as supply and personnel management. Moscow, as the Soviet capital, has its own air defense district.

The air defense regiments of the Soviet Union's Warsaw Pact allies are fully integrated within the Soviet system. Overall command of these forces is exercised by Soviet rather than national officers and

PREVIOUS PAGES: The design of the Vostok space launcher owes much to the SS-6 Sapwood, the world's first ICBM.
BELOW: The ubiquitous MiG-21 has chalked up over 25 years' service with Frontal Aviation, but is being replaced by the MiG-23 Flogger.

there is no separate air defense organization for the individual East European states. In Soviet eyes they are simply outposts of the Soviet Union's air defenses, which enable enemy bombers and interdiction aircraft to be engaged before they cross the Soviet frontiers. Nonetheless, Warsaw Pact air defense forces operating over their homelands are likely to prove more reliable in action than non-Soviet forces committed to an offensive. For this reason the non-Soviet Warsaw Pact air forces are invariably stronger in interceptor regiments than in tactical fighter units. For example Poland currently deploys eleven interceptor regiments and only six tactical fighter regiments. Even the reliable East Germans are primarily defensively equipped, with their air force organized into two air defense divisions primarily equipped with MiG-21 fighters and surface-to-air missiles. There are only two East German *Kampffliegergeschwadern* (equivalent in size to Soviet aviation regiments), which fly the elderly Su-7 Fitter. What little modern equipment reaches the East European air arms is generally for air defense purposes.

The medium-to-high altitude, 185 mile range SA-5 Gammon SAM has recently been deployed in the area. Two sites are believed to be in East Germany, near Rostock and Rudolstadt, another in western Czechoslovakia and a fourth in western Hungary. Hitherto only the much shorter range SA-2, SA-3 and SA-4 have been deployed this far forward. It may be that the NATO deployment of stand-off reconnaissance and surveillance systems such as the Boeing E-3 Sentry and Lockheed TR-1A, has led to this move. It has also been suggested that the SA-5 has an anti-missile capability and if this is true its forward deployment is then more likely to be linked to NATO's introduction of the Pershing II.

The shooting down of the Korean Airlines Boeing 747 Flight 007 over the Sea of Japan on 1 September 1983 focussed the world's attention on the Soviet Air Defense Forces. The interception was carried out by two Su-15 Flagon and four MiG-23 Flogger air defense fighters, and it was one of the former which brought down the airliner with an air-to-air missile. In Soviet eyes this was a perfectly legitimate action in defense of her territorial integrity. Not only had the airliner strayed from an international

air route and flown into Soviet airspace, but it had penetrated a highly sensitive (and therefore heavily defended) region. The Sea of Japan is a sanctuary area for the Soviet Pacific Fleet's 14 Delta-class SSBNs, whose missiles can reach targets in the United States from a launch point within home waters. Yet this was not the only reason for Soviet

sensitivity to violations of its airspace in this region.

The Korean Boeing's deviation from its assigned flightpath coincided (quite literally incredibly in the Soviet view) with a night test of the new SS-X-25 ICBM, which was targeted on the Kamchatka peninsula. This test had attracted the attention of an American Ferret-D ELINT satellite, which was backed up by a SAC RC-135 aircraft operating in international airspace. Add to this the well established practice of Aeroflot airliners conducting reconnaissance missions over Western military installations and the Soviet decision to shoot down the airliner is explained. There is no reason to suppose that a miscalculation resulted from a mis-identification of the Boeing 747 airliner as a military RC-135. Both military and civil aircraft have been intercepted and fired on by Soviet air defense fighters in the past. One incident in 1978 involved – coincidentally – a Korean Airlines Boeing 707 which approached the Northern Fleet's heavily defended base area on the Kola Peninsula and was fortunate to make a forced landing after coming under fire from Soviet interceptors. The Soviet view of such incidents is that its Air Defense Forces are

TOP: A radar controller vectors the fighters to their targets.
ABOVE: Sukhoi's Su-15 Flagon interceptor is both larger and more powerful than the MiG-21, possessing also a limited all-weather operating capability.
LEFT: East Germany's two air defense divisions still rely on the MiG-21 to supplement their air-to-air missiles.

71

shown to be operating efficiently by the book in defense of the homeland. Heads would roll if such incursions were not intercepted.

The key to the successful employment of interceptors and SAMs in air defense is radar early warning and control. The Soviet Union is not an easy country to provide with adequate radar coverage, due to its sheer size and to the special problems presented by its long and inhospitable Arctic frontier. Nonetheless the Air Defense Forces controls some 7000 military radars, which provide early warning of both missile and air attack, airspace surveillance for the control of interceptors, and target acquisition data for SAMs and AA artillery. Additional coverage is provided by a small force of airborne early warning aircraft, which is at present being modernized and probably expanded. Satellite systems too contribute to early warning of missile attack and civil air traffic control radars contribute to the surveillance of Soviet airspace.

It is the early warning satellites which provide the Soviet Union's first line of defense against attack by ballistic missiles. Like their American counterparts, they rely on sensitive infra-red detectors to pick up the flare from the ICBMs' rocket motors as they leave their launching silos. However, unlike the United States' satellites which cover the Soviet ICBM fields from geostationary orbit above the equator, the Soviet satellites follow highly elliptical, semi-synchronous orbits. When the satellites reach the high point of these orbits over the North Atlantic they appear to hover over the earth for a period of about five hours and during this time they can scan the American ballistic missile fields and transmit data back to the Soviet Union. Similar coverage of the Chinese launching sites is possible as the satellites cross over the Western Pacific.

House radars, a new system of phased-array radars is being constructed. Each having a range of about 1250 miles, the new radars are being sited around the Soviet borders and it is believed that a total of ten are planned. A new phased-array radar has also been added to Moscow's ABM defenses. It is a massive four-sided structure, each face standing 120ft high and measuring 500ft across, and provides 360-degree radar coverage. It is sited at Pushkino on the outskirts of the Soviet capital.

The first-generation Soviet anti-ballistic missile is the ABM-1B Galosh, which since the abandonment of the United States' Safeguard system in 1975 is the only operational weapon of its kind in the world. Galosh is believed to be a three-stage missile with a launch weight of around 72,000lb. Range is quoted as over 200 miles and the missile is fitted with a nuclear warhead of around 2 megatons yield. The 32 missiles are sited in four launch complexes, each with eight missiles, distributed around Moscow. Recent reports indicate that the missiles are now housed in protective silos, but since the radars that they depend upon for guidance remain highly vulnerable, the justification for this measure is not immediately apparent. Soviet research and development work on new ABM systems is extensive and reports that new ABM sites are being built in the Moscow area suggest that a second generation of ABMs is about to be deployed. This may be a combination of long- and short-range missiles to provide a layered defense. Two new ABMs which have been reported to be under test could make up such a system. The SH-4, which may be a development of the Galosh, is a long range missile able to 'loiter' at high altitude while ground radars discriminate between real and decoy warheads. SH-8 is a hypersonic missile which could intercept those warheads which had escaped destruction by the longer-range ABM and had reentered the earth's atmosphere. It is unlikely that this missile carries a high-yield nuclear warhead. The new missile site phased-array radar at Pushkino may be associated with the SH-8.

An extensive network of ground-based radars and control centers directs the Air Defense Forces' interceptors. However, with the deployment of air, sea and ground-launched cruise missiles by the United States, the Soviet air defenses must be prepared to deal with numerous small, low-flying targets. The conventional ground-based radar is ill-suited to such a task. Even the USAF's ageing B-52 bombers, with their relatively poor low-altitude flying characteristics and massive radar 'signatures,' are difficult targets for such a defense system. Therefore the pressing need is for the Air Defense Forces to introduce a new airborne warning and control aircraft to provide the long-range detection capability against low-flying targets which the present Tu-126 Moss airborne warning aircraft lacks. Such an aircraft, based on the Il-76 Candid tactical transport and codenamed Mainstay by NATO, is about to enter service. It is not likely to lack for targets for, apart from the proliferation of cruise missiles, the USAF's new B-1B bomber will become operational in 1986. Not only is it a faster aircraft than the B-52, with much improved low flying characteristics, but it also has a considerably reduced radar signature. Yet the greatest challenge of all will come in the 1990s, when Strategic Air Command's Advanced Technology Bomber appears. Its 'stealth' technology is claimed to make it invisible to radar and the aircraft's infra-red emissions, engine noise and even its visibility will be much reduced. Such an aircraft

The launch warning satellites have only recently become operational and their surveillance complements that of three over-the-horizon backscatter radars, which can also detect ICBMs as they are launched. Two of these radars, located at Minsk in the western USSR and at Nikolayev-na-Amur in eastern Siberia, are directed against the United States. Because of the problem of radio wave propagation in Arctic regions (which has deterred the United States from employing a similar system to guard its northern approaches), the Soviet OTH-B radars are positioned as far to the east and west as practicable to avoid the worst of these effects. The third Soviet OTH-B radar at Nikolayev in the Ukraine covers the Chinese missile launching sites.

Once the enemy missiles have climbed above the radar horizon (conventional radar beams follow a line of sight) they are acquired and tracked by the Soviet Union's 3700-mile-range Hen House radars. These cover approaches from the west, east and southeast and partially from the south and are used to provide early warning for Moscow's ABM defenses. From the radars' coverage it is clear that the Soviet ballistic missile defenses are primarily concerned with threats from the British, French and Chinese nuclear forces. In any case it is obvious that the limited Soviet ABM system, comprising only 32 missiles, could easily be swamped by United States warheads. Also associated with ballistic missile defense are the intermediate range (1700 mile) Dog House and Cat House radars, together with the Try Add ABM missile control radars. In order to supplement this coverage and fill in the gaps left by Hen

During the decade which followed Moss's entry into service, the Soviet Union has made great advances in electronics and computer technology, although in these areas it still lags well behind the United States. Nonetheless, it has sufficiently mastered the techniques of pulse-doppler radar and computer processing of raw radar data to enable a Soviet airborne warning and control system with a 'lookdown' capability to be developed. This is based on a modified Il-76 Candid transport's airframe, fitted with a rotating radome above the fuselage. It has been given the NATO reporting name Mainstay and is now in production for the Air Defense Forces. Total production of 50 or so Mainstays is anticipated by Western observers.

The number of interceptor aircraft available to the Air Defense Forces is around 2500, although some reports of the recent Soviet air reorganization suggest that half these aircraft have been reassigned to Frontal Aviation. Nonetheless they will continue to operate in the air defense role, as with the exception of the MiG-23 Flogger, which can undertake air superiority missions and has a secondary ground-attack role, all are specialized interceptors with little capability in fighter-versus-fighter combat. In parallel with the changes in organization within the Air Defense Forces, there has been a fundamental

ABOVE: Although Mikoyan's MiG-25 Foxbat is to be superseded in the interceptor role by the improved and developed MiG-31 Foxhound, the older type's near Mach 3 performance will keep it in service as a reconnaissance type.

threatens to make the complex and costly Soviet air defenses obsolete overnight.

For the immediate future though the Air Defense Forces must concentrate on mastering the threat from low-flying aircraft and cruise missiles. The capabilities of the Tu-126 Moss airborne early warning aircraft are limited to the detection of targets at medium and high altitude. This is hardly surprising in an aircraft which first entered operational service in 1970, seven years before the United States E-3 Sentry. It is in fact unlikely that the Tu-126 was intended to detect low flying targets against ground clutter, although one American assessment credits the aircraft with a marginal effectiveness against such targets over water. The Tu-126 was most probably designed to fill the gaps in ground radar coverage, especially along the Arctic frontier, and to operate in conjunction with Tu-28P Fiddler long-range interceptors as a forward air defense system. The ten Tu-126s at present in service with the Air Defense Forces are conversions of the four-turbo-prop Tu-114 airliner. The Tu-126 carries an early warning radar in a saucer-shaped radome atop the fuselage and is also fitted with ESM (electronic support measures) equipment, which enables it to detect radio and radar emissions from enemy aircraft at long range. Any data derived from these sensors will probably be transmitted to ground control stations and in addition the Tu-126 will carry its own fighter controllers to direct interceptions. One of the aircraft's most useful attributes is its long endurance (some 20 hours) and this can be extended by in-flight refueling. Consequently it is probable that the Moss has accommodation on board for a relief crew. The Tu-126 can also be used as an airborne control center to direct attack and bomber aircraft against their targets from stand-off ranges. A single Moss demonstrated this capability during the Indo-Pakistan War of 1971, when it was loaned to the Indians together with its Soviet crew. However, there are no indications that the Air Defense Force's small fleet of Tu-126s would support Frontal Aviation in a similar manner in wartime.

reassessment of operational doctrine. Formerly Soviet air defense pilots operated under rigid ground control with all tactical decision-making taking place in the control center and the pilot merely reporting and carrying out instructions. This is still the preferred method, as it maintains the inflexible subordination to higher authority so beloved of Soviet military doctrine. However, it has been increasingly recognized that improvements in airborne radars and in the range and effectiveness of air-to-air weapons enable a single fighter to operate as an autonomous unit. Furthermore, an interceptor pilot who is totally dependent on instructions from the ground can easily be neutralized by enemy communications jamming. Consequently a new emphasis on individual initiative has appeared in Soviet writings on fighter doctrine. An air defense pilot, writes Colonel-General I Meskvitelev, 'should be able to operate at an enormous distance away from the airfield, in any weather, to operate, if need be, independently, that is without any advice from the ground and independently take decisions... It is essential to assess a situation instantly and take the only correct decision.'

The Air Defense Forces operates a diverse force of interceptor aircraft, which at present comprises seven distinct types. The more modern designs such as the MiG-25 Foxbat-E and MiG-23 Flogger-G have a limited 'lookdown-shootdown' capability which enables them to engage low-flying targets. In this respect the MiG-31 Foxhound-A is much improved, as will be the Su-27 Flanker and MiG-29 Fulcrum due in service in the mid 1980s. Over 40 percent of the inventory are modern fighters and the numbers of such older types as the Su-9 and Su-11 Fishpot, Yak-28P Firebar and Tu-28P Fiddler are being run down as the newer fighters come into

ABOVE: A Tupolev Tu-28 Fiddler development aircraft, pictured in 1961. It became the largest fighter in the world when it entered service, though the ventral fairing and fins seen here did not appear on production examples.

LEFT: A trio of missile-armed Fiddlers climb to altitude. A mixture of infra-red and radar-homing AA-5 Ash missiles comprised the type's usual armament.

service. The interceptors of the Air Defense Forces can be reinforced with fighters assigned to Frontal Aviation's regiments if necessary. Such switching of assets between two different armed services has been made much easier by the command reorganization of the early 1980s.

With an absolute maximum speed of Mach 3 (reduced to Mach 2.8 when air-to-air missiles are carried) the MiG-25 Foxbat is the most impressive of the Soviet interceptors in terms of sheer perform-ance. It was originally designed to counter the USAF's B-70 Valkyrie bomber, which was to have operated at Mach 3 at 70,000ft altitude. Yet despite the cancellation of the American bomber program, development work on the MiG-25 continued and it produced a highly-specialized interceptor. Powered by two Tumansky R-31 turbojets, each producing 27,000lb thrust with afterburning, the MiG-25 has an initial rate of climb of 30,000ft per minute and a service ceiling of around 75,000ft. Its missile arma-ment comprises four AA-6 Acrid AAMs, one version being infra-red homing and another semi-active radar homing. These are usually fired in pairs, with the radar-guided missile having a maximum range of 30 miles and the IR version half that distance. The MiG-25's Fox Fire radar has a 60-mile detection range. Thus the initial production version of the MiG-25 interceptor (code-named Foxbat-A by NATO) can scramble from ground alert and engage a bomber target flying at high altitude 500 miles away within a period of less than half an hour. However, in order to achieve this performance much of the versatility desirable in a combat aircraft

has been sacrificed. The Foxbat-A performs and handles poorly at low altitudes and maneuverability is limited at all heights. The Foxbat could certainly not engage in fighter-versus-fighter combat.

Despite the MiG-25's limited usefulness, around 250 of these high-altitude interceptors are in service (in addition to 150 of the tactical reconnaissance versions). The initial production version, the Fox-bat-A, is currently being converted to Foxbat-E standard with a new radar, which gives the fighter a limited capability to engage low-flying targets from above. A far better 'lookdown-shootdown' perform-ance is obtained from the MiG-31 (or possibly MiG-25M) Foxhound. Foxhound is in full production for the Air Defense Forces and two regiments had been equipped with the type at the end of 1983. It is a two seat interceptor, based on the design of the MiG-25, but it is fitted with a pulse-doppler radar and has the second crew member to operate it. Its maximum speed of Mach 2.4 is appreciably less than that of the Foxbat, but this is offset by an increase in combat radius. Missile armament comprises four AA-9 radar-guided missiles, which can 'snap down' to engage low-flying targets. Maximum engagement range is about 25 miles and targets flying as low as 150ft have been successfully intercepted during tests. Thus the Foxhound/AA-9 combination appears to be well suited to countering cruise mis-siles. Shorter range weapons carried by the MiG-31 include four AA-8 Aphid dogfighting missiles and a heavy cannon (the Foxbat-A has a detachable ventral gunpack). The AA-8 is a 4-mile range, highly maneuverable dogfighting missile, which is

ABOVE: Developed from the Su-15, the Su-21 Flagon-F interceptor is distinguishable by its double nosewheel unit.
LEFT: A Mikoyan MiG-23 Flogger fighter trails its braking parachute on landing.
BELOW: An underside view of a MiG-25 Foxbat in Libyan service. It carries a pair of AA-6 missiles under the wing.

also carried by the Air Defense Forces' Su-15 Flagons. It may be that by fitting such missiles to its less maneuverable interceptors, the Air Defense Forces seek to compensate for their sluggishness with the missile's agility.

The multi-role MiG-23 also serves in the interceptor role in its Flogger-B and Flogger-G versions. The latter is fitted with a new radar to give it a limited ability to engage low-flying targets and some of the Flogger-Bs may also be so equipped. A variable-geometry wing fighter, the Flogger has a maximum speed of Mach 2.2 at 36,000 feet and is supersonic at sea level. Thus it is a considerably more versatile interceptor than the Foxbat.

Standard missile armament comprises two AA-8 Aphids and two medium-range (20 mile) AA-7 Apex AAMs, plus a twin-barrel 23mm cannon. Apex is a relatively large and heavy missile for its performance class and is usually carried in mixed pairs of semi-active radar-homing and infra-red-guided variants. Over 2000 MiG-23 Floggers are in Soviet service (plus 650 ground-attack MiG-27 Floggers) and the type has entirely superseded the MiG-21 in the Air Defense Forces' interceptor regiments. However, MiG-21 Fishbeds do remain in service with Frontal Aviation and with the air forces of the Warsaw Pact allies. The fighter's high speed (Mach 2) and exceptional maneuverability make it an effective (although now aged) air superiority fighter and interceptor, though its usefulness in the latter role is limited by its poor range and limited-range weapons.

Second in importance only to the MiG-23 in terms of the numbers in service is the Su-15 Flagon (750 currently deployed), a large twin-engined, delta-wing interceptor. This became operational in the late 1960s and it began life as a progressive development of the Su-9/Su-11 Fishpot. However, it emerged as a much larger and heavier aircraft, with only a modified version of the earlier interceptors' wing to reveal its ancestry. Maximum speed of the Su-15 is over Mach 2 and combat radius is some 400 miles. The Flagon's primary mission is as a bomber interceptor and its standard armament in this role is two 14-mile range AA-3 Anab AAMs, one radar guided and the other IR-homing. However, in recent years attempts have been made to improve the Su-15's close-range armament by fitting it with AA-8 Aphid dogfighting missiles and twin

retained in service as advanced training aircraft.

The Tu-28P Fiddler and Yak-28P Firebar long-range interceptors of 1960s' vintage remain in service in some numbers, with around 200 Yak-28Ps in the Air Defense Forces' inventory and half that number of Tu-28Ps. However, they are likely to be phased out during the mid 1980s as increasing numbers of Foxhounds become available. The Tu-28P is the largest fighter in the world, with a length of 85ft, span of 65ft and 85,000lb maximum take-off weight. It can attain a maximum speed of Mach 1.8 and operate over a combat radius of 800 miles. It carries a crew of two, a pilot and radar operator to manage the 32-mile range Big Nose radar. Armament is four infra-red and radar-homing AA-5 Ash AAMs with a maximum range of 18 miles. The Fiddler is especially designed to mount a forward defense of the Soviet Union's inhospitable Arctic frontiers, but in common with the other Soviet interceptors of its era it lacks the ability to engage low-flying targets. The Yak-28P Firebar carries out a similar mission in the less important air defense districts. It is a two-seat, Mach 1.8 interceptor, which is armed with two AA-3 Anab AAMs. With a similar main armament to the Su-15 but a much improved endurance, it fills a gap in capability between the Flagon and the Tu-28P Fiddler.

Although the older Soviet interceptors are only of limited use against the current generation of Western bombers, interdiction aircraft and cruise missiles, they can nevertheless be usefully employed in guarding the Soviet Union's troubled frontier with China. The problems of intercepting low flying aircraft will be much eased by the deployment of the new MiG-29 Fulcrum and Su-27 Flanker in the mid 1980s. The latter is a Mach 2.3 all-weather fighter fitted with beyond-visual-range AAMs and having a full 'lookdown-shootdown' capability. The MiG-29 is a rather smaller aircraft and is faster and more maneuverable, but will also be effective against low-flying targets. Clearly it is somewhat better suited to Frontal Aviation's air superiority mission than the Su-27 – the more so because it may well have a secondary ground-attack capability. Yet both Frontal Aviation and the Air Defense Forces are in need of the new fighter aircraft and so production deliveries are likely to be divided between the two users. The first MiG-29s were reported to be delivered to the Air Defense Forces in 1983 (presumably for service testing).

ABOVE: Some 200 examples of the 1960s-vintage Yak-28P Firebar long-range interceptor remain in service. They will be replaced by the MiG-31 Foxhound.

Aircraft Strength of Air Defense Forces		
Type	Role	No:
MiG-25 Foxbat	Interceptor	250
MiG-23 Flogger	Interceptor	800
Su-15 Flagon	Interceptor	750
Su-9/11 Fishpot	Interceptor	400
MiG-31 Foxhound	Interceptor	30
Tu-28 Fiddler	LR Interceptor	90
Yak-28 Firebar	LR Interceptor	200
Tu-126 Moss	AEW	10
Il-76 Mainstay	AEW	?

Note: Several hundred interceptor aircraft may have passed from Air Defense Forces to Frontal Aviation during 1983.

gunpods on the underfuselage pylons (which are seldom used to carry auxiliary fuel tanks). The earlier Su-9/Su-11 Fishpot is being phased out of service, although as many as 400 were in use in the early 1980s. Both are Mach 2 interceptors with only a limited all-weather capability, the Su-11 having an improved radar and AAMs. The survivors may be

RIGHT: Artist's impressions of two of the newer additions to the Soviet armory, the Sukhoi Su-27 Flanker (on ground) and the MiG-29 Fulcrum (airborne).

The diversity of the Air Defense Forces' interceptor inventory is matched by that of its surface-to-air missiles. These consist of both fixed systems for the strategic air defense of vital areas of the Soviet homeland and mobile systems which provide a tactical air defense umbrella over the Soviet armies in the field. Within the Soviet Union there are some 10,000 SAM launchers distributed among 1400 fixed sites, which cover major population centers, industrial regions and important military installations. High, medium and low altitude bands are covered by these missiles, but as with the interceptor force the emphasis has recently been on developing effective low-level systems. There has also been an improvement in the ability of the Air Defense Forces' SAMs to engage multiple targets simultaneously. The air defense troops serving with the ground forces are similarly equipped with a range of missiles, able to engage targets at all altitudes and most of the 9000 or so anti-aircraft artillery pieces (ranging in caliber from 23mm up to 130mm) are deployed with these units. The field armies' air defenses are as much the concern of the Air Defense Forces as are the strategic systems, but since the former constitute an integral part of tactical air operations, they are more fully discussed in Chapter Five of this book.

The oldest surface-to-air missile in the Soviet inventory (and incidentally one of the first SAMs to be deployed anywhere in the world) is the SA-1 Guild. Since its introduction in the mid 1950s, the SA-1 has formed part of Moscow's missile defenses, with a double ring of launchers emplaced around the city. It is a medium-altitude missile and is believed to be fitted with an active radar homing system and has a range of some 30 miles. SA-1s are currently being phased out of service and replaced by the SA-10. The new missile is a considerably more effective weapon with double the range of the SA-1 and the ability to engage targets at low, medium and high altitudes. Its capability against low-level aircraft and cruise missiles is especially valuable and the SA-10 is associated with a tower-mounted surveillance radar for early acquisition of such targets. The missile may also have a secondary anti-ballistic missile role, as it has been reported that test firings have been made against ICBM reentry vehicles. In addition to its deployment around Moscow, the SA-10 has been emplaced to cover high value targets elsewhere in the Soviet Union.

The well-known SA-2 Guideline missile remains operational at some 400 sites in the Soviet Union. It was widely deployed by the Air Defense Forces during the 1960s and saw considerable combat use with the Egyptians in the Middle East wars and with the Vietnamese during the Southeast Asia conflict. It is a medium-altitude missile with a range of some 30 miles and carries a 300lb high explosive warhead.

ABOVE: The long-serving SA-1 is only now being retired from the Soviet SAM armory. When this photograph was taken in 1966 the type had already clocked up a decade in service.

Each missile site generally comprises six SA-2s emplaced around a central radar and control center complex. Although by no means entirely ineffective, the SA-2 is vulnerable to ECM jamming and can be outmaneuvered in flight by tactical fighter aircraft. During the Vietnam War it was found that between 50 and 150 SA-2s had to be fired to shoot down one aircraft. However, the missile's greatest value is probably in denying enemy aircraft the use of medium altitude heightbands and forcing them to fly low where the problems of navigation and target acquisition become considerably greater.

Low-altitude point air defense of high-value targets is provided by the SA-3 Goa, a 12-mile range SAM fitted with a 130lb high explosive warhead. This missile is deployed at over 300 sites within the Soviet Union and it is also employed by the Warsaw Pact allies. Each launcher is fitted with either two or four missiles, the majority in Soviet service being quadruple units. The SA-3's 50-mile range Low Blow control radar is able to guide two missiles onto the same target simultaneously. As with most Soviet missiles fired from fixed sites, it is easily transportable by truck. However, unlike the mobile missiles which can be fired from their transporters, it must be transferred to a launcher before firing. Nonetheless, this does give the Air Defense Forces some flexibility

in deployment. The North Vietnamese, presumably following the guidance of their Soviet advisers, frequently shifted the positions of their SAM sites during the Southeast Asia War.

The Air Defense Forces' longest range missile by a considerable margin is the 185-mile SA-5 Gammon, which is effective at medium and high altitudes up to about 100,000ft. It has a launch weight of some 22,000lb and is fitted with a 130lb high explosive warhead. Guidance is by radio command and the missile reaches a maximum speed of over Mach 3.5. More than 100 SA-5 launch complexes are operational within the Soviet Union and Eastern Europe, with around 1000 individual launchers deployed. The identified sites at Tallinn in the Estonian SSR on the Gulf of Finland and in Eastern Europe suggest that the SA-5 is deployed at forward positions along the Warsaw Pact frontiers. Some idea of the missile's capabilities can be gained from the concern expressed over the safety of Lockheed U-2s operating from Cyprus, when it was announced that two SA-5 sites had become operational in Syria. The Air Defense Forces recognize that the SA-5 sites are likely to be targets for air attack and so they are protected by low/medium-altitude SA-6 and SA-8 missiles.

The most recent Soviet strategic SAM system to

enter service is the SA-12, which made its appearance in 1983. This is a versatile missile which can engage targets at low, medium and high levels (from 100ft up to 100,000ft) out to a range of 60 miles. The missile guidance radar is a phased array system, which can deal with a number of targets at the same time. SA-12s based in East Germany have been reported to have an ABM role against the recently deployed Pershing II. Two other Soviet SAM systems, the SA-5 and SA-10, are alleged to have a secondary ABM capability. They could be used in conjunction with the large phased array radars currently under construction, as the basis for a much expanded ballistic missile defense system. This in essence is the contention of American critics of Soviet adherence to arms control accords. Yet, while it is probably true that the new phased array radars could be used for ABM battle management and that the SA-5, SA-10 and SA-12 have a limited capability against missile warheads during reentry, this falls well short of a nationwide ABM defense.

LEFT: The SA-12 and its radar system is supremely versatile, being able to operate at all levels against multiple targets and apparently also having an ABM capability.
BELOW LEFT: SA-3s are easily transportable, but must be transferred to a launcher before firing.
BELOW AND BOTTOM: ZSU-23-4 four-barrelled cannon provide a valuable complement to SAM defenses. The 23mm guns are radar directed and, being mounted on a tank chassis, the system is very mobile.

If there are to be any dramatic breakthroughs in ballistic missile defense technology, they are likely to come not with improved anti-ballistic missiles, but through the deployment of directed-energy beam weapons in space. The Soviet Union has been working on such systems for several years, but a considerable amount of research and development is needed before an operational beam weapon can be put into space. In the early 1980s a retired Chief of USAF Intelligence, who ought to have known better, claimed that by the middle of the decade the Soviet Union would have the capability of destroying all American satellites and most of its ballistic missile forces with directed-energy weapons. A more sober and realistic assessement is that a laser-beam anti-satellite weapon could be deployed in space by the Soviet Union in the early 1990s, but that a space-based ABM system could probably not be operational until the turn of the century.

The Soviet Union has an extensive space program, launching between 75 and 100 space vehicles each year. About 80 percent of these are military vehicles and many of the scientific space missions also have military value. All five armed services have an interest in the space program; the Air Defense Forces use satellites for early warning of ICBM attack; the Strategic Rocket Forces require satellite survey data for precise targeting of their missiles; the Navy makes considerable use of satellites for sea surveillance and even missile guidance; while all services benefit from space communications, meteorological, navigational and intelligence gathering systems. Space launches are carried out by the Strategic Rocket Forces from three complexes, the main one at Tyuratam, with others at Plesetsk and Kapustin Yar. These three sites are heavily defended by interceptor airfields and SAM complexes of the Air Defense Forces.

It has been estimated that 85 percent of Soviet space missions perform military functions, many of them being joint civil research and military projects.

LEFT: SA-4 Ganef SAMs roll through the Moscow streets on a May Day parade. The missile has a range of some 40 miles, and can operate at medium/ high altitudes.

BELOW: The infra-red-guided SA-9 Gaskin is developed from the hand-held SA-7 and is mounted in two quadruple launchers on an armored personnel carrier chassis.

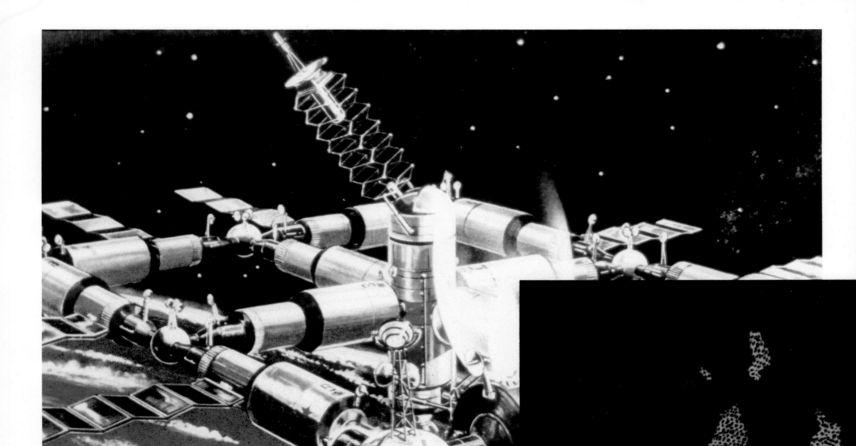

This intensive level of space activity contrasts with a much more modest United States military effort in space. Each year the Soviet Union launches payloads totalling 660,000lb into space, a weight ten times greater than that launched by the United States. This statistic is only partly the result of a greater Soviet interest in the military possibilities of space, however, because it also reflects to some degree Soviet technical backwardness. Two military space missions illustrate this point. Firstly, a comparison between Soviet and American early warning satellites shows that whereas the United States can perform this task with three satellites, the Soviet Union requires nine satellites. Furthermore, the Soviet Union has suffered many EW satellite failures and so has had to increase its launch rate yet further to replace defective vehicles. Secondly, in the field of space reconnaissance the United States has produced satellites with operational lives of five months (Big Bird) and one year (KH-11), where as the Soviet reconsats operate for much shorter periods (typically 14 days or 44 days). However, the Soviet Union does have an impressive lead in manned flight in space, with twice as many man-hours in orbit than the United States and a record 211-day mission to its credit.

Many of the Soviet space missions are boosted into orbit by launch-systems derived from ballistic missiles. Such obsolete missiles as the SS-4 Sandal, SS-5 Skean, SS-6 Sapwood and SS-9 Scarp have all been modified as space boosters. While this practice has the great advantage of making use of existing resources – and the Soviet forces are notably reluctant to scrap any system which has a vestige of remaining usefulness – it does have the drawback that individual payloads are small. Even the booster derived from the mighty SS-6 Sapwood has only a 15,500lb payload (that based on the SS-9 is slightly less), while that of the American Saturn V is around 640,000lb. Yet in terms of operational capability, it is clearly useful to have a large stock of boosters readily available, so that space missions may be launched at short notice to meet unforeseen contingencies.

Nonetheless, the Soviet Union has apparently recognized that specialized boosters are needed to support its space program. The three boosters of the D1 family now in service have a payload of around 48,500lb and a new family of space launchers will provide greater payloads and flexibility. These consist of two conventional boosters; one a medium-lift vehicle with a 28,500lb payload, the other a heavy-launch booster in the Saturn V class capable of lifting 330,000lb. The third is a reusable vehicle similar in concept to the American Space Shuttle,

but having twice the payload (130,000lb). However, the Soviet shuttle is probably a decade away from operational service and thus the United States has an important lead in the use of reusable space launchers. However, the Soviet Union has already tested a small reusable 'space plane,' pictured elsewhere in this volume. Its mission is not known, but the United States is interested in such a vehicle as a 'space fighter' and it may be that the Soviet Union is working along similar lines.

Once the new generation of Soviet heavy-lift boosters come into service, it is probable that they will be used to establish a large manned space station in earth orbit. Much of the Soviet manned space effort appears to be directed towards this end. Soviet cosmonauts have already carried out three missions lasting more than six months each and the Salyut-6

BELOW: The Soviet anti-satellite ASAT weapon is depicted in action. Yearly tests have been carried out to maintain the weapon's efficiency, but it is only effective at present against targets in low earth orbit.

ABOVE: The familiar Ilyushin Il-18 airliner provided the basis for the Coot-A electronic intelligence aircraft with a suspicious-looking ventral bulge containing much extra equipment.

OPPOSITE TOP AND RIGHT: A small scale model of a Soviet space plane is recovered from the Indian Ocean after a test flight.

space station has been used to demonstrate the techniques of resupply and crew exchange in space. These efforts may well culminate in a permanent Soviet presence in space from 1990 onwards. The military applications of such a space station would certainly include reconnaissance and it is most probable that Soviet cosmonauts (most of them military officers) have already carried out such missions during manned flights. Less obvious advantages of manned stations are the opportunities it gives of testing equipment and materials in space which will be used later in unmanned satellites. In the future too are more warlike missions, such as the direction of anti-satellite and ABM weapons from an orbiting space command post. By the end of the century it seems likely that space will have become a battleground for the superpowers. Perhaps this will be signalled by the space force becoming the sixth branch of the Soviet armed forces.

For the immediate future, however, space will continue to be primarily a vantage point from which to survey the earth. Of all the current military space missions reconnaissance and surveillance are by far the most significant. There is no area of the earth's surface which cannot be surveyed from space, using a variety of techniques including photography, infra-red and radar sensing and electronic reconnaissance. The information gathered can be used to assess the strength of enemy strategic and tactical forces, to determine their peacetime dispositions and in time of crisis to monitor their reactions. Strategic arms limitation agreements would probably never have been concluded unless the signatories were confident of verifying their opponent's activities by satellite reconnaissance. The accurate targeting of strategic missiles is largely dependent upon data derived from satellite reconnaissance and space systems are increasingly being investigated as possible tactical target acquisition systems. Indeed it is believed that the Soviet Union already uses spacecraft to provide mid-course guidance for its long-range anti-shipping missiles.

Soviet photographic reconnaissance satellites return exposed film to earth for processing by capsules both at the end of the mission and, in the case of those reconsats which remain in orbit for more than a month, at two points during the mission.

This method produces photographs of better resolution than those transmitted from the satellite to a ground station. Yet it has the disadvantage that there is a time gap of perhaps as much as two weeks between the taking of the photograph and its interpretation and so timely intelligence may thereby be lost. The satellites employed on 14-day missions have a dual intelligence-gathering role and an earth-resources mission over Soviet territory. The long-endurance satellites are purely military systems and there are generally three or four of them in operation at any one time. Their orbits can be altered on command from a ground station in order to cover areas of particular interest. Alternatively they may be programmed to follow the same ground track on each orbit.

The greatest disadvantage of photographic reconnaissance (including infra-red photography) is that it is totally dependent upon clear weather over the target. No such limitations apply to ELINT satellites, which detect radar and radio emissions. The military value of these systems is considerable, as radio transmitters and radars are essential components of all modern military command and control systems. Therefore the locations of army, naval and air units can be pinpointed from their electromagnetic emissions and analysis of the signals picked up will reveal much information about their composition, capabilities and readiness states. Furthermore, the data gathered by ELINT satellites, together with that from other EW monitoring systems, on enemy radar and radio operating frequencies will be of great value in planning electronic countermeasures. The Soviet ELINT satellites are placed in circular orbits at an altitude of some 400 miles above the earth. Six of them are operational continuously, each having a life of around eighteen months and replacements are invariably launched before failures occur.

Radar too is unaffected by cloud cover, although the resolution obtained is generally too poor for it to be a substitute for photo-reconnaissance. However, it is valuable for surveillance missions and the Soviet Navy uses Rorsats (radar ocean reconnaissance satellites) for locating – and probably targeting – ships at sea. The Rorsat carries a powerful radar, which can cover a 300-mile wide area of the earth's surface. The power-source for this sensor is a nuclear reactor carried on board the satellite and it was one such spacecraft – Cosmos 954 – which achieved notoriety in 1978 when it scattered radioactive material over a wide area of northern Canada after its reentry. Rorsats are not continuously in orbit, but are specially launched when needed. Their appearance usually coincides with large-scale Soviet naval exercises. The Soviet Union may be developing a surveillance satellite capable of detecting aircraft in flight, perhaps using infra-red detection as does the United States' Teal Ruby project. Such a system would certainly help to resolve the problems of guarding the vast areas of Soviet airspace.

Other military satellites are used for communications, navigation and meteorology. Soviet satellites for communications relay comprise the Molniya series, which occupy a highly elliptical orbit, and the Gorizont, Raduga and Ekran satellites in geostationary orbit. The Molniyas have been in use since the early 1960s and are now being superseded by the later systems. This process of increasing use of comsats for military command and control is likely to continue throughout the decade and will probably result in the Soviet armed forces becoming as

dependent on these systems as the United States services are at present with some 80 percent of all messsages being transmitted by satellite. The Soviet Union also lags behind the United States in the use of navigational satellites and, although the Soviet Navy makes use of such a system, there is no indication that a Soviet equivalent of the American Navstar GPS system is being developed. Meteorological satellites primarily perform a scientific function, but can provide weather data which is essential for the planning of military operations. On average there are four Meteor-2 metsats in orbit, transmitting data to three main receiving stations in the Soviet Union.

At present the most impressive Soviet military space system is undoubtedly its ASAT (antisatellite) weapon, which is capable of destroying enemy spacecraft in near-earth orbit (at altitudes of up to 1000 miles). It is basically an interceptor satellite which is boosted into an orbit which will pass close to that of its victim. Once within range, the ASAT detonates a warhead which will pepper its target with fragments. The ASAT system was proved to be extremely accurate during initial testing and practice interceptions are carried out at yearly intervals to maintain the satellite interceptor's operational efficiency. However, the ASAT is only effective against satellites in low earth orbit and, while this may put reconsats at risk, the EW satellites and comsats vital to the United States' strategic defense are at present not in danger. The system makes use of a modified SS-9 booster and is thought to be operational at the Tyuratam missile test center. A 'killer satellite' for use against targets in geosynchronous orbit is reported to be under development.

The Soviet Union has an impressive list of space achievements to its credit, including the first artificial satellite in orbit and the first manned spaceflight. Despite the handicap of a less advanced scientific, technological and industrial base than the United States, it has consistently employed its available resources imaginatively and skillfully. There is no doubt that it was the first to realize the potential decisiveness of space-based ABM weapons and to devote an intensive research effort into developing such a system. The next two decades will show whether this foresight will pay dividends.

The greater part of the Soviet Air Force's strength is concentrated within Frontal Aviation, a hard-hitting tactical air force with a strength of more than 5000 combat aircraft organized into 112 aviation regiments and seven independent squadrons. The greater part of this force is made up either of ground-attack fighters or of dual-role air superiority fighters with a secondary attack capability. In addition some 700 aircraft perform the tactical reconnaissance and electronic warfare roles. The 2300 combat helicopters assigned to army support are also part of Frontal Aviation, but because they constitute in effect a Soviet army air arm they are dealt with separately in the following chapter. Frontal Aviation is organized into tactical air commands within the 16 Soviet military districts and the four groups of Soviet forces in Eastern Europe. Although these were formerly numbered air armies, since the early 1980s they have been more closely integrated with the military command structure of the ground forces they support. Thus each theater of military operations has its aviation commander and assigned air regiments, which form a integral part of its force structure rather than being attached units drawn from a parallel air force command system as in the past. The great advantage of the new system is that resources can be grouped within the theater according to military need, rather than to conform with the strict geographical boundaries of Army Fronts and Air Armies.

Frontal Aviation's actions in support of ground forces can be classified as air or anti-air operations, according to the definitions of Marshal Ogarkov writing in the *Soviet Military Encyclopedia*. The aim of the air operation will be to strike at vital enemy installations throughout the depth of his defenses and thus the battlefield interdiction attacks of Frontal Aviation will be coordinated with the

deeper missions of AASU's interdiction aircraft and medium bombers. The desired result of the operation will be to achieve the maximum possible disruption to enemy forces from the outset of hostilities, thus facilitating the rapid advance of the armies. It is likely that this operation – at any rate initially – will use conventional ordnance rather than tactical nuclear weapons. However, the aims of both nuclear and non-nuclear strikes are essentially similar, although conventional air strikes will need to be made in much greater force to achieve the same results. Thus American analysts anticipate that a Soviet air operation against the NATO Central Region could involve a force of 2400 aircraft, with individual strike waves being 300 to 400 aircraft strong. The targets for Soviet massed air attacks will certainly include enemy nuclear forces, always a priority for Soviet operations even when they do not anticipate using these themselves.

Even before the deployment of Pershing II missiles to West Germany at the end of 1983, Frontal Aviation was exercising its MiG-27 Floggers, Su-17 Fitters and Mi-24 Hind-D attack helicopters against these targets. Next in importance would probably be enemy air defense radars and surface-to-air missile belts, so that gaps could be opened to allow penetration into the enemy rear areas. Not only would fighter-bombers make direct attacks on these systems, perhaps using special anti-radiation missiles against the radars, but ECM aircraft would also attempt to jam the radars. Tactical airfields would most probably also be priority targets for attack, especially if that attack were directed against NATO. The Soviet Air Force must certainly recognize that its fighters will be outclassed in air combat by such aircraft as the F-15 Eagle and to a lesser degree the F-16 Fighting Falcon. Therefore if a proportion of these enemy fighters can be destroyed

PREVIOUS PAGES: Cutaway artwork of Sukhoi's variable-geometry Su-17 in its Fitter-D variant.
BELOW: The Flogger-F version of the MiG-23 incorporates the slimmer nose profile of the MiG-27 ground-attack type.

on the ground the odds will be evened at the lowest risk to Soviet aircraft. Yet even if the individually more capable Western fighters escape destruction on their airfields, they are unlikely to meet Soviet air superiority fighters in a one-versus-one contest. Soviet fighters outnumber their NATO counterparts by five-to-one. So, even if these odds are lessened by reinforcements from the United States, the Soviet Air Force is likely to have the advantage of greater numbers of fighters. Their object will be to defeat the enemy air forces as swiftly as possible and thereafter to concentrate on their secondary ground attack missions in support of the army. Fire support for the armies will in any case be a primary mission for the ground attack fighters, which make up over one-third of Frontal Aviation's strength.

It is by no means certain that all of the objectives of the Soviet air operation can be attained even by the massed forces of Frontal Aviation. However, complete destruction of the enemy's tactical nuclear forces, his air defense missile belts, tactical airfields and his ground forces is clearly an unrealistic aim and, although Soviet commanders will probably plan to eliminate the enemy's tactical nuclear capability entirely, other target systems will be attacked more selectively. For example, only those tactical airfields from which the most modern NATO fighters operate need to be eliminated, as the older Western fighters such as the F-4 Phantom, F-104 Starfighter and BAC Lightning can be more evenly matched by the Warsaw Pact in air combat. Similarly, only those portions of the enemy SAM defenses or ground armies which present an immediate threat to Soviet air forces need be eliminated. Furthermore, if enemy headquarters and their command and control systems are effectively knocked out, the forces that they direct will lose much of their cohesion. Such target planning will require both extensive and accurate tactical reconnaissance if it is to be successfully carried through. Therefore great demands will be made on Frontal Aviation's 640 reconnaissance aircraft. Yet, while not denying that an effective air operation will involve a massive effort from Frontal Aviation, it must be acknowledged that other important forces will contribute to the overall operational plan. These will include raiding forces provided by *Spetsnaz*, airborne and heliborne troops, together with deep-ranging Operational Maneuver Groups, fire from conventional artillery and perhaps strikes by tactical missiles fitted with high-explosive or chemical warheads. The combined efforts of all these forces are likely to cause considerable disruption behind enemy lines and, combined with the pressure of a rapid frontal ground and air assault, could well result in an early Soviet victory.

While the primary aim of the air operation is to take the war to the enemy's forces throughout the depth of his territory, the anti-air operations' objective is to safeguard Soviet forces from similar disruption. The Soviet high command realizes that in a war against NATO forces (or indeed against the US Rapid Deployment Force in the Middle East) the enemy will fully exploit the flexibility and striking power of his air forces in an attempt to blunt the initial Soviet attack and so gain time to enable effective ground defenses to be established. These tactics can in part be countered by the Soviet Air Forces' own offensive operations against enemy air installations and so the air and anti-air operations are to some degree interdependent. Soviet forces can also be safeguarded by deploying a forward

ABOVE: A Soviet Su-17 takes off. The type is flown in the attack and reconnaissance roles by Frontal Aviation, and (attack only) Naval Aviation.

screen of air superiority fighters, which will have the dual role of covering friendly ground attack aircraft and intercepting enemy air strikes. A last line of defense for the Soviet ground forces is provided by their own air defense umbrella of tactical SAMs and antiaircraft artillery. Such passive measures as effective camouflage, dispersal of forces and maintaining proper intervals between vehicles in convoy will also help to reduce the effectiveness of any enemy air action.

Clearly one of the reasons for the far-reaching reorganization of Soviet tactical air power in the early 1980s was the recognition of the close relationship between Frontal Aviation's air regiments and the ground forces that they support. Another was the considerably improved capabilities of the new generation of Soviet combat aircraft which appeared during the 1970s. With the introduction into service of the Su-24 Fencer the Soviet Union gained a hitherto unattainable capability for low-level, deep penetration interdiction missions. In the MiG-27 Flogger-D it acquired a highly effective ground attack aircraft, capable of carrying 4400lb of ordnance over a range of 400 nautical miles – simultaneously doubling both the payload and range of the aircraft it replaced. Lastly, with the appearance of the MiG-23 Flogger-B air superiority fighter, Frontal Aviation gained an aircraft with better endurance than the short-range MiG-21. Moreover, unlike the MiG-21 which was armed only with short range air-to-air missiles and cannon, the MiG-23 was able to engage targets beyond visual range with its medium-range AAMs, while retaining the earlier fighter's short-range armament. The significance of the new tactical warplanes of the 1970s was that they enabled the Soviet Air Force to conduct offensive operations throughout the depth of the enemy's territory for the first time. Frontal Aviation was transformed from a largely defense

BELOW: Although it entered service around 1974, the Su-24 Fencer was not seen outside the Soviet Union for some years. Now over 600 are estimated in service in Europe and the East.

orientated air superiority fighter force, having only limited attack capabilities, into a more balanced multi-role tactical air arm.

In many ways the epitome of the new generation of Soviet warplanes, the MiG-23/27 Flogger family has given the Soviet Air Force the sort of dual role air-to-air and air-to-ground combat capability which the F-4 Phantom gave the USAF in the 1960s. With over 2500 Floggers in service with the Air Force and Air Defense Forces, it is now the most widely used Soviet warplane. The two main versions

LEFT: The Su-25 Frogfoot ground attack aircraft was blooded in action in Afghanistan before deployment in Europe.

LEFT: A Sukhoi Su-17 unleashes a salvo of air-to-ground missiles.

LEFT: A Sukhoi pilot prepares for action.

are the MiG-23 interceptor and air superiority fighter, which has a secondary ground attack mission, and the specialized MiG-27 attack aircraft. Both have the same basic airframe and variable-geometry wing, with a sweepback angle of between 17 degrees and 72 degrees. The wing design enables the Flogger family to combine the good payload/range characteristics demanded by a multi-role fighter with the ability to operate from roughly

surfaced tactical airstrips. Apart form such specialized types as the Su-24 Fencer and MiG-25 Foxbat reconnaissance aircraft, most Soviet tactical aircraft have this capability.

The initial production version of the Flogger was the MiG-23S (Flogger-B), which is intended primarily for air-to-air combat. Initially its armament comprised infra-red and radar-homing AA-2 Atolls and AA-2-2 Advanced Atolls inherited from the earlier MiG-21 Fishbed. However, these 4-mile-range missiles were later replaced by a combination of two AA-7 Apex medium-range AAMs and four AA-8 Aphid short-range missiles. There is also a built-in, twin-barrel 23mm GSh-23 cannon with a rate of fire of 3000 rounds per minute. The radar capabilities of the Flogger have also been progressively improved, as the initial production version's 50-mile-range High Lark has been replaced on the later Flogger-G by a pulse-doppler radar with a limited 'lookdown-shootdown' capability. Powerplant performance has also been improved, with the 22,500lb thrust Tumansky R-27 turbofan giving way on later aircraft to the 25,300lb thrust R-29B. The more powerful engine improves the MiG-23's acceleration and sustained turn rate, but in maneuverability is is no match for the F-15 Eagle or F-16 Fighting Falcon. In stand-off engagements the MiG-23 can outrange the F-16, which at present has no medium-range missile armament, but again it is markedly inferior to the F-15 both in missile range and radar detection range. Nor can it match either American fighter in the pilot's visibility from the cockpit, as the view from the MiG-23 both downward and rearward is especially poor. Consequently, the Flogger's preferred fighter tactics will be medium- range missile engagements rather than dogfighting.

Whereas the MiG-23 fighter can operate up to an altitude of 55,000ft and has a maximum speed of Mach 2.2 at 36,000ft, the ground attack MiG-27 is optimized for low-altitude operations. Its engine inlets are fixed in contrast to the MiG-23's variable inlet ramps and the engine exhaust nozzles are simplified in design. As a result, although the MiG-27 is as fast as the MiG-23 at sea level at Mach 1.1, its maximum speed at 36,000ft is only Mach 1.6. The MiG-27's forward fuselage is entirely redesigned, as with the deletion of the air interception radar the nose contours have been considerably slimmed down to improve downward visibility from the cockpit. Weapon release is assisted by a simple ranging radar and a laser-rangefinder in the nose.

ABOVE: The Czech Air Force is one of the chief customers for the MiG-23, which has been exported both within and outside the Warsaw Pact.

ABOVE: A cutaway artwork of the Mikoyan MiG-23 with wing, nose radar and engine detail clearly visible

Maximum ordnance load is 6600lb and a Gatling-type multi-barrel cannon replaces the GSh-23. Large 'doughnut' tires are fitted to the MiG-27's main wheels to improve rough-field operations and attachment points for rocket-assisted take-off packs are fitted to the rear fuselage for the same reason. Two versions of the MiG-27 have been identified, the initial production Flogger-D and the later Flogger-J with improved avionics. There is also a hybrid version, the MiG-23BM Flogger-F, which has the nose modifications of the MiG-27 but retains the MiG-23's engine arrangement. The hard-hitting MiG-27 has twice the range and twice the payload of the Su-17 Fitter-C, which entered service only five years before the Flogger-D appeared in 1975.

The MiG-21 Fishbed was, like the Flogger, the most widely-used Soviet fighter of its generation. However, far from being a versatile aircraft, it was essentially a very maneuverable interceptor and air superiority fighter which lacked the payload and range necessary for the ground attack mission. Nevertheless, progressive improvements to the MiG-21F Fishbed-C of 1959 have resulted in a more workmanlike light fighter design, with some all-weather and ground-attack capability. Some 700 later-model MiG-21s remain in service with Frontal Aviation's fighter regiments, with a further 130 being used for tactical reconnaissance. The latest MiG-21bis Fishbed-N is primarily valuable as a forward-based air superiority fighter, which is able to take on the maneuverable Western fighters in close-range dogfighting combat while the MiG-23 operates from stand-off ranges. As such it is essentially a stop-gap expedient, pending the availability of the MiG-29 Fulcrum. Compared with the F-16 Fighting Falcon the MiG-21bis has a similar maximum speed (Mach 2) and much the same rate-of-climb, but the American fighter has twice the rate of turn of the MiG-21 at low level. However, this disadvantage can be offset to some degree by arming the MiG-21 with the highly-agile AA-8 Aphid air-to-air missile, which can pull 30 g (a force equivalent to thirty times that of gravity) during maneuvers. The MiG-21 usually carries a pair of infra-red homing AA-8s, together with two radar-guided AA-2-2 Advanced Atolls, plus a built in GSh-23 cannon with 200 rounds of ammunition.

The MiG-29 Fulcrum is a twin-engined, dual role air combat and ground attack fighter, broadly similar in concept to the US Navy's F-18 Hornet. According to USAF Intelligence sources the aircraft became operational at the end of 1983 (rather earlier than previously expected), but has not yet reached the fighter regiments in quantity. It is credited with a 'lookdown-shootdown' capability and combines a long range with the high thrust-to-weight ratio needed for maneuverability in air combat. Armament probably comprises a combination of two medium-range 'snapdown' radar-guided AA-9s and two AA-8 Aphids together with a built-in cannon. An infra-red dogfighting missile with a performance similar to that of the American AIM-9L Sidewinder is known to be under development and may well arm later versions of the MiG-29. Maximum speed for the Fulcrum is quoted as Mach 2.8, but if this is correct it probably applies to a lightly-loaded test aircraft in 'clean' condition. Operational aircraft are more probably capable of about Mach 2.5. The MiG-29 will certainly be a considerably more agile aircraft than the MiG-23, with an instantaneous turn rate of 16.8 degrees per second compared to the Flogger-B's 11.5 degrees per second. The Su-27 Flanker is primarily intended for beyond visual range engagements with AAMs and can detect and destroy low flying targets. American sources credit it with a capability similar to the F-15 Eagle, and an instantaneous turn rate of 23 degrees per second has been quoted for the fighter.

The ground attack and battlefield interdiction missions are shared equally between the MiG-27 Flogger-D and -J variants and the Su-17 Fitter-D and -H variants with about 650 of each in service. There are also about 150 of the earlier Su-7BM Fitter-As remaining in front-line units. The standard Soviet strike fighter of the 1960s, the Su-7BM is a large single-seat swept-wing fighter powered by a single 22,000lb thrust Lyulka AL-7 turbojet. Maximum speed at low level is Mach 1.1 in 'clean' condition, but range is limited and even when carrying two auxiliary fuel tanks is only some 900 miles. Because of the need to carry fuel tanks on the underfuselage pylons, only the four wing hardpoints are available for ordnance and this effectively restricts the weapons load to 2200lb. In addition there are two heavy-caliber 30mm cannon mounted in the wing roots, each with 70 rounds of ammunition. Apart from its short range, the Fitter-A's most notable deficiency is the absence of modern navigation and weapons aiming equipment. However, within its limitations it is an effective aircraft, which performs well at low altitude and is a steady weapons aiming platform. Both the Indian and Egyptian Air Force pilots who have flown the type in combat have testified to its qualities as a robust ground attack aircraft, well able to absorb battle damage and return to base.

The Su-17 is an adaptation of the Su-7, fitted with variable-sweep wing outer panels and a more powerful engine. As a result of these comparatively inexpensive changes, which in no way compare to the costs or the disruption in production deliveries of putting an entirely new aircraft type into service, the Soviet Air Force has acquired a considerably enhanced ground attack capability. Compared with the Su-7, the Su-17 can lift twice the ordnance load over a distance 30 percent greater and it can operate from much shorter airstrips. The new aircraft can also deliver ordnance with greater accuracy, as it is fitted with ranging and terrain avoidance radar, a laser rangefinder and marked target seeker and a weapons release computer. Like its predecessor, the Su-17 handles well at low level and the Su-7's twin cannon armament is retained. Ordnance loads may include air-to-surface missiles and AA-2 Atoll AAMs for self-defense. Compared with the MiG-27, the Su-17 is a much less effective aircraft as its combat radius and payload are half that of the later ground attack fighter. However, in practice the two

BELOW: A Sukhoi Su-7 Fitter-B takes off. The Su-7's limited range, even with external tankage, restricted its applications.

aircraft are complementary as the Su-17 will carry out short range close air support sorties, leaving the MiG-27 free to undertake the more demanding battlefield interdiction mission.

The latest Soviet ground attack aircraft is the Su-25 Frogfoot, a small, twin-engined ground attack aircraft armed with a 30mm rotary cannon and up to 8800lb of ordnance. It is essentially a short-range, clear-weather, battlefield support aircraft in the tradition of the wartime Il-2 *Shturmovik*. The type made its operational debut over Afghanistan in 1982 and, although it was deployed in two regiments to Bulgaria in early 1984 and now also serves with the Czechoslovakian Air Force, its characteristics are better suited to the counter-insurgency war in Afghanistan than to the much more demanding conditions in the West. Consequently Su-25s may mainly be restricted to the Southern and Far Eastern theaters, where air opposition is likely to be slight and the aircraft's lack of the avionics required for the low-level, all-weather attack mission is less of a handicap. Comparisons with the USAF's A-10 Thunderbolt II are misleading in many ways. The Su-25 is a smaller aircraft with a shorter range and it carries less ordnance. Furthermore its 30mm cannon, although of the same caliber as the A-10's GAU-8, is almost certainly not a similar specialized tank-killing weapon. Therefore the Su-25 is unlikely to have been conceived as a specialized anti-armor aircraft for Central Europe. In any case, while the A-10's anti-tank tactics make sense for a force operating on the defensive over friendly territory, they are less workable for a force on the offensive – and Soviet military doctrine seems little concerned with the fighting of defensive battles.

Soviet ground attack aircraft can make use of a wide range of free-fall and precision-guided munitions. Standard weapons include 500kg (1100lb) and 250kg (550lb) high-explosive bombs and 57mm unguided air-to-ground rockets in 8-, 16- and 32-round pods. More specialized bombs include a rocket-assisted anti-runway concrete 'dibber' and a

weapon intended to penetrate NATO's hardened aircraft shelters. It is known that Frontal Aviation has made use of laser-guided bombs since 1981 and there are probably electro-optically guided 'smart bombs' in service as well. Other likely Soviet developments in air-to-ground ordnance include cluster-bomb dispensers and fuel-air munitions. Tactical air-to-surface missiles include the laser-guided AS-10, which is carried by the MiG-27, Su-17 and Su-24. It has a range of some six miles and cruises at Mach 0.8. A larger and heavier laser-guided missile, the AS-X-14, is being developed and this will have a considerably greater range. At present the AS-7 Kerry is the most widely used Soviet tactical ASM. It has a range of six miles and is guided by a radio command link to the launch aircraft. Much longer ranges are obtainable from anti-radiation missiles, which home onto radar emissions. The AS-9 is able to launch an attack from a distance of 50 miles and a new missile with three times this range is under development. The successor to the AS-7 is likely to achieve a 25-mile maximum range making use of inertial mid-course guidance and an electro-optical seeker for terminal homing. All these weapons have conventional high-explosive warheads and tactical nuclear weapons will be free-fall bombs.

It is more likely that Soviet fighters will deliver chemical weapons rather than nuclear bombs, at any rate during the early days of a conflict. The Soviet army includes over 80,000 chemical defense troops and, since NATO would only employ such weapons in retaliation for Soviet first use, the implication is that these troops are expected to deal with contamination caused by their own forces. Soviet tactical fighters can deliver such nerve gases as Sarin and Soman either by spraying or by bombs. Chemical weapons would probably be used against enemy front-line troops during an assault, or against tactical airfields. Quite apart from the casualties caused amongst unprepared personnel, chemical weapons would greatly reduce overall efficiency by

ABOVE: Touching down after a mission, this Su-7BMK exhibits rocket-assisted take-off (RATOG) bottles under its rear fuselage for operation from limited-length runways.

forcing the survivors to wear cumbersome and restrictive NBC protective suits for long periods. All equipment would have to be decontaminated, thus leading to further interference with operations, and in all probability chemical weapons would be used together with high-explosive bombs to hinder such damage control measures as airfield runway repair. Clearly, chemical warfare will play a part in any major Soviet offensive, as it will probably result in just the sort of disruption that Soviet military doctrine seeks to achieve. Chemical attack will bring many of the tactical benefits of battlefield nuclear weapons without the danger of nuclear retaliation (although chemical weapons may well be used in reprisal). It is believed that chemical weapons may comprise as much as 30 percent of Soviet munitions stocks.

The effectiveness of the Soviet Air Force's ground attack missions is not solely dependent on the characteristics of the weapons that they will use, but will also depend on the weapons delivery skills of the aircrew. Soviet training philosophy differs from that of most Western air forces in that their pilots receive short periods of intensive training rather than this being a continual process. A recent trend has been to improve the realism of Soviet air-to-ground training. For example it is known that the Soviet weapons range at Rossow incorporates a dummy airfield target which is laid out to simulate the USAF base at Bitburg in West Germany. Significantly, Bitburg houses the F-15 Eagles of the 36th Tactical Fighter Wing and the F-15 is the one Western air superiority fighter which conspicuously outmatches its Soviet counterparts in every respect. Therefore it is likely that the Soviet Air Force has special plans to eliminate these aircraft on their airfield. Air-to-surface missile firings have also been exercised intensively by Frontal Aviation, with an average of 2000 such practices each year. Another recent

development has been the attention given to the ground control of close air support sorties, a skill that was for many years neglected by the Soviet forces. In general, ground attack missions will be tailored to the characteristics of the available Soviet aircraft, with armed helicopters carrying out close air support in the vicinity of friendly troops, Su-17s operating near the forward edge of the battle area and MiG-27 Floggers taking on the battlefield interdiction mission.

Tactical air reconnaissance will be of vital importance to Soviet commanders at all levels. It will identify enemy defensive positions and troop movements for the ground forces and will locate mobile enemy targets for air attack and carry out post airstrike assessments. Frontal Aviation has a force of 640 reconnaissance aircraft, comprising 150 MiG-25 Foxbat-B and -Ds, 160 Su-17 Fitter-Hs, 130 MiG-21 Fishbed-Hs and 200 Yak-28 Brewer-Ds. Reconnaissance sensors include cameras, infrared linescan and sideways-looking radar and data from the latter may be transmitted to ground stations as it is obtained to give 'real time' intelligence. In addition to the manned aircraft, the Soviet Union also uses a battlefield surveillance drone, the DR-3.

The fast and high flying MiG-25 Foxbat is undoubtedly the most effective Soviet reconnaissance aircraft. Operating at Mach 3 at altitudes up to 75,000ft, it presents a difficult target even for the most modern interceptors such as the F-15 with missiles capable of 'snap up' engagements and it is effectively beyond the reach of the older air defense fighters. Two versions are in service: the Foxbat-B equipped with cameras and the Foxbat-D, which has a large sideways-looking radar. There are five cameras carried in the nose of Foxbat-D, one mounted vertically with the others at angles of 15 degrees and 45 degrees pointing both to port and

starboard. This arrangement can cover an area 40 miles wide from the Foxbat's maximum operating height. The sideways-looking radar has an even wider coverage of some 60 miles and the Foxbat-D is probably also equipped to carry out electronic intelligence. A Foxbat-B deployed to Egypt in 1970-71 reconnoitered the Sinai peninsula and much of Israel in just four flights. Low level reconnaissance will be carried out by the Fishbed-H and Fitter-H, both of which are fitted with pod-mounted reconnaissance systems. The twin-engined Yak-28 Brewer-D, with a maximum speed of Mach 1.1 at medium altitude, is probably employed over low-threat areas where the risk of interception is small.

The electronic-warfare version of the Yak-28, the Brewer-E, is much better able to take care of itself, as its sizeable internal weapons bay (able to accommodate 4500lb of bombs in the attack version) is packed with ECM jammers. Because of its limited speed, it is likely to act as a stand-off stystem in support of strike aircraft rather than as an ECM escort. However, carefully orchestrated tactics should ensure that it is in position to blind those radars which are the greatest danger to a strike force at the outset of their mission. The Cub-C EW version of the An-12 tactical transport, with a payload of up to 44,000lb, has a considerably greater capacity as a stand-off jamming system. It has been reported that a force of around 40 of these aircraft will operate against NATO's Hawk SAM radars from 60 miles inside Warsaw Pact territory. This jamming effort is intended to allow Soviet strike aircraft to penetrate NATO's defensive missile belt. It is likely also that the Soviet Union is able to jam NATO's IFF (identification, friend or foe) equipment, making it difficult for the defense to distinguish enemy from friendly fighters.

Quite apart from the specialized electronic warfare aircraft, most Soviet tactical fighters are fitted with ECM equipment. The standard Sirena-series radar warning receivers fitted to the MiG-23/27 Flogger, Su-9 and Su-17 Fitters and MiG-21 Fishbeds alert the pilot to the presence of a hostile radar and indicate its bearing from the aircraft. This allows him to take appropriate countermeasures, which may involve evasive maneuvering, the release of chaff (strips of metalized foil which blot out a radar screen with their echoes), or initiating jamming. It is believed that the Soviet Air Force employs both jamming pods and ECM jammers built into their aircraft. However, little is known about these systems, although in general the Soviet Union has a high reputation for effective electronic countermeasures – founded on the known capabilities of its land and naval systems.

The tactical air defense of field formations is provided by the *Voyska*-PVO (Troops of the Air Defense Forces). It is made up of a mixture of AA guns and SAMs which provide a layered defense from ground level up to some 65,000ft throughout the depth of the army's positions. As a result of their weakness in effective fighter cover in the early years of the Great Patriotic War, the Soviet forces relied instead on anti-aircraft artillery to a degree far greater than that of any other nation. This philosophy continued during the postwar years, when mobile and transportable missiles took the place of most of the AA guns. Although the Soviet forces have never tested their tactical air defense missiles in action, the Egyptian Army did use the Soviet system during the Yom Kippur War of 1973. It proved very effective in countering the numerically and qualitatively superior Israeli Air Force during the opening days of the war, when Israeli aircraft losses were high and the damage inflicted on the Egyptian troops by air attack was minimal. However, in the course of the conflict this situation altered as the Israelis made increasing use of

BELOW: Two photo-reconnaissance MiG-25R Foxbats of the Trans Baikal Military District line up on the runway. The nearer aircraft is a Foxbat-B, the other a Foxbat-D.

dovetail so neatly together in theory. The danger has been lessened with the gradual retirement of transportable missiles such as the SA-2 and SA-3 in favor of truly mobile units mounted on tracked or wheeled launch vehicles. Nonetheless, even though missile crews no longer have to go through the time-consuming process of transferring missiles from their transport truck onto launchers and then back again during every move, weaknesses remain. For example many missiles cannot be fired from a launcher while it is moving and so, as some units move forward, others must remain in place to provide cover. Another problem may arise during river crossing operations, for whereas few of the tactical SAM launch vehicles are amphibious (the SA-8 vehicle is an exception), many of the armored vehicles and APCs that they accompany will be.

One of the most effective weapons against low-flying aircraft and especially helicopters is the ZSU-23-4, a four-barrelled 23mm radar-directed AA cannon mounted on a tank chassis. Low-altitude coverage will also be provided by SA-8, SA-9 and SA-13 SAMs mounted on vehicles and the man-portable SA-7. The SA-8 Gecko, a five mile

ABOVE: The widely-used SA-2 Guideline.
RIGHT: The hand-held SA-7 is effective against low-flying aircraft, and has also been used by terrorists to down civilian targets.

American-supplied electronic countermeasures jammers, anti-radiation missiles and stand-off ASMs. Therefore, while the Soviet ground-based tactical air defenses are not the complete answer to the problems of defending army forces from air attack, they can seriously limit the effectiveness of ground-attack aircraft.

One danger that the Soviet air defense commanders will have to guard against is that as the armies advance rapidly into enemy territory, a number of his SAM and AA units will fall behind. This will cause holes to appear in the air defense umbrella formed of mutually supporting short and medium-range weapons, whose areas of effective fire

Aircraft Strength of Frontal Aviation

Type	Role	No:
MiG-23 Flogger	Air Superiority	1200
MiG-21 Fishbed	Air Superiority	700
MiG-29 Fulcrum	Air Superiority	?
MiG-27 Flogger	Attack	650
Su-17 Fitter	Attack	650
Su-7 Fitter	Attack	150
Su-25 Frogfoot	Attack	25
MiG-25 Foxbat	Recce	150
MiG-21 Fishbed	Recce	130
Su-17 Fitter	Recce	160
Yak-28 Brewer	Recce	150
Yak-28 Brewer	ECM	40

range missile, is mounted in fours on its wheeled launch vehicle, which also carries search and tracking radars. The SA-9 Gaskin is a development of the SA-7 Grail, both being infra-red guided, and is carried in two quadruple launchers on a modified armored personnel carrier. SA-9s are in the process of being replaced by the infra-red SA-13. These short-range systems will be deployed to cover troops in forward positions from attack by such threats as anti-armor helicopters and terrain-hugging close air support aircraft such as the USAF's A-10 Thunderbolt II. They will also be useful in guarding columns on line of march, especially at such choke points as defiles and bridges, where they will be especially vulnerable.

Medium-altitude SAMs are able to operate from further behind the forward line of troops, as their ranges are considerably greater than those of the low-level missile. The SA-4 Ganef, with a range of over 40 miles, is effective at both medium and high altitudes. The missiles are carried in pairs on a tracked launcher vehicle and are accompanied by Long Track and Pat Hand surveillance and missile control radars. The 20-mile range SA-6 Gainful is a more compact missile, weighing less than a third of the SA-4's 4000lb launch weight. SA-6s are carried in threes by a modified PT-6 tank chassis. The SA-11 which was operationally deployed in the early 1980s is mounted in fours on the same chassis as that used by the ZSU-23-4. Its maximum range is about 20 miles and it can engage targets at heights of 45,000ft down to around 100ft, giving it a useful dual medium and low altitude capability. Unlike the earlier more cumbersome medium-altitude SAMs, the SA-11 will probably be deployed with forward troops to obtain the maximum advantage from its low-altitude performance.

There can be little doubt that the Soviet armies will be able to cover their advancing forces with an intense barrage of fire from AA artillery and missiles. However, what may be questioned is their ability to command and control this immense concentration of firepower under the chaotic conditions of the modern battlefield. The diversity of Soviet air defense weapons is in some respects a strength, as it compounds the problems of the attacking air force in devising countermeasures and evasive maneuvers. Yet on the other hand, it does make the job of exercising centralized control a somewhat more complicated proposition.

Apart from ensuring that no gaps appear in the air defense coverage, friendly aircraft must be positively identified and provided with safe corridors through the defenses. The problem of maintaining effective control of forces is not confined to the tactical air defenses, however. One of the great imponderables of modern warfare is whether the Soviet high command will be able to maintain its rigid direction of ground and air forces in the maelstrom of combat.

BELOW: SA-6 Gainful SAMs are normally seen mounted on modified tank chassis.
BOTTOM: The SA-3 Goa will soon be replaced altogether by more mobile weapons systems on tracked or wheeled launch vehicles.

CHAPTER SIX

BATTLEFIELD HELICOPTER FORCES

One of the cornerstones of Soviet military doctrine is the necessity of attacking the enemy's forces throughout the depth of their deployment, coordinating raids on the rear areas with frontal assaults to achieve the maximum disruption and damage to matériel and morale. Raiding parties may vary in composition and strength from a small group of *Spetsnaz* (special forces) troops up to an entire airborne assault division, but among the most effective will be heliborne assault troops operating most probably in battalion or brigade strength. The Soviet Army has only comparatively recently discovered the great advantages to be gained in tactical mobility through helicopter airlift. Certainly during the 1960s when the US Army was conducting massive air-mobile helicopter operations in Vietnam, the Soviet Union had no comparable capability. However, a new awareness of the potential of helicopters could be seen by their imaginative employment during the Ethiopian War in 1978. During the battle for Jijiga, the Soviet commander General V I Petrov used his helicopters to lift men and armored vehicles over a mountain barrier to take the Somali defenders in the rear. In that year the Soviet

PREVIOUS PAGES: Since its introduction in 1974, the Mil Mi-24 transport/gunship has revolutionized Soviet helicopter warfare. A Hind-F with fuselage-mounted cannon armament is pictured.
BELOW: The giant Mi-6 lifts a tractor. The fixed wing is detachable, but serves the purpose of offloading the rotor when heavy objects are to be carried.

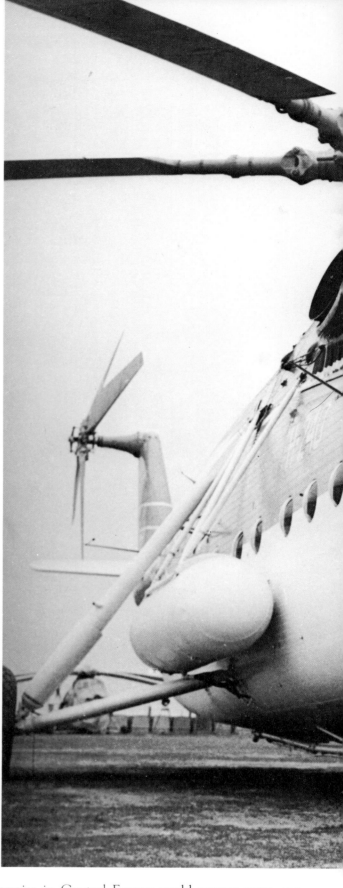

armies in Central Europe could muster some 400 tactical helicopters, but within five years this force had doubled in strength. This increase was made in spite of the demands of the counter-insurgency war in Afghanistan, in which helicopters are arguably the most effective weapons at the disposal of the Soviet occupation forces.

Soviet battlefield helicopters are a part of the Air Force's Frontal Aviation command, rather than being an independent army air arm. The distinction is largely an academic one, however, as the integration between helicopter forces and army formations

is close. For example, it is believed that each of the five helicopter regiments of the Air Forces of the Group of Soviet Forces in Germany is assigned to one of the GSFG's five armies. What this arrangement does illustrate is that the recent reorganization of Soviet tactical air power has resulted in so close a link between the ground forces and their air support that the Soviet Army thinks it unnecessary to have the helicopter regiments transferred to its control from the Air Force. Frontal Aviation controls a total of 3450 helicopters, of which about 2300 are combat helicopters with the remainder being used for such duties as liaison and scouting. The heavily-armed Mi-24 Hind serves in both assault transport and attack roles, with about 800 in use. There are 1500 Mi-8 Hip assault transports and 400 of the heavier Mi-6 Hook cargo transports in service. The massive Mi-26 Halo heavy lift helicopter has recently come into use and the balance of the force is made up by 750 Mi-1 Hare, Mi-2 Hoplite and Mi-4 Hound helicopters for miscellaneous support duties.

The helicopter regiment is made up of three squadrons, each of which comprises three flights, and there is a regimental headquarters flight equipped

ABOVE: When designed in the mid 1950s, the Mi-6 was the world's largest rotorcraft.

with liaison and scouting helicopters. The strength of each regiment varies according to its role and the importance of the military districts to which it is assigned. A strength of between 60 and 85 helicopters has been reported for an assault helicopter regiment (operating Mi-24 Hinds), while a transport helicopter regiment's strength varies between 42 and 66 (Mi-8 Hips and Mi-6 Hooks). However, the composition of the regiments serving with the Group of Soviet Forces in Germany is likely to be different, because they must provide the army commanders both with fire support and troop transport. Consequently they are likely to be composite units flying both Hind attack helicopters and transport types. It is possible that the more specialized helicopters, such as the Mi-24 Hind-D and E attack

BELOW AND BOTTOM: Mi-24 Hind-Ds are readied for flight. The Hind-D boasts a four-barrel nose-mounted 12.7mm machine gun, visible in both photographs, with rocket pods and missile stations on the type's stub wing.

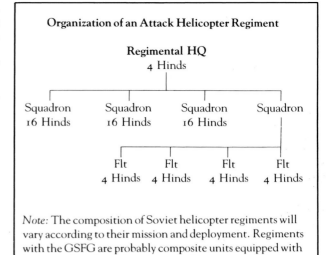

Organization of an Attack Helicopter Regiment

Regimental HQ
4 Hinds

Squadron	Squadron	Squadron	Squadron
16 Hinds	16 Hinds	16 Hinds	

Flt	Flt	Flt	Flt
4 Hinds	4 Hinds	4 Hinds	4 Hinds

Note: The composition of Soviet helicopter regiments will vary according to their mission and deployment. Regiments with the GSFG are probably composite units equipped with both attack and assault transport helicopters.

helicopters and Mi-6 Hook and Mi-26 Halo heavy lift types, operate in independent squadrons.

Until recently there were no Soviet troops specially trained for helicopter assault operations. Instead standard motor rifle regiments were required to provide a battalion for such missions as the need arose. Since only a few hours' training is needed to teach troops the techniques of working from helicopters, this practice means that an assault force can be readily assembled at a moment's notice. However, one disadvantage of this lack of specialization is that once in action the troops would have less support from the fire of armored personnel carriers and artillery than they are accustomed to expect. A number of APCs and artillery pieces will be lifted into the landing zone by heavy transport helicopters, but their numbers will perforce be limited. Since it was clearly desirable to have a force of specially trained air-mobile troops available in order to ensure that objectives of particular importance were effectively dealt with, the Soviet Army has accordingly formed eight air-mobile brigades. These units are regarded as special reserves and they are assigned directly to the theater commanders. In Central Europe one such brigade is based at Cottbus

in East Germany. It has a strength of some 2500 men organized into four rifle battalions, plus a supporting artillery battalion and reconnaissance, anti-tank, signals and transport companies. Two of the four rifle battalions are trained as paratroop units. Clearly these are highly trained shock troops, who will be reserved for assaults on key objectives. Therefore it is likely that the Soviet Army will continue to make use of troops drawn from the motor rifle regiments for most assaults. In any case its helicopter troop lift capacity at present far exceeds the strength of the air-mobile brigades.

Although the primary reason for the growth of Frontal Aviation's combat helicopter units in the late 1970s was undoubtedly in order to increase the tactical mobility of ground units, one outcome of this expansion has been to provide the Army with a new form of fire support in the armed attack helicopter. The attack helicopter was an innovation of the Vietnam War and was originally intended to provide fire support and armed escort for troop carrying helicopters. It was found that a specialized attack helicopter was needed to lay down suppressive fire before and during landing operations, as this was when the troop-carrying machines were most vul-

nerable to ground fire. In Vietnam the USAF was reluctant to allow the Army's attack helicopters to develop their close air support potential to the full, as this trespassed on a jealously-guarded Air Force preserve. In contrast the Soviet forces appear ready to adopt any weapon that is likely to perform a mission effectively, irrespective of the service to which it belongs. Consequently they have adopted the attack helicopter as a close air support weapon,

TOP: This Mi-6 bears the livery of the Soviet airline Aeroflot, but the distinction between military and civil aircraft means little.
ABOVE: Mikhail Mil's first postwar success, the piston-engined Mi-1.

ABOVE: An early exercise in air/ground co-operation is carried out by a flight of Mi-1s.
RIGHT: Having disgorged troops and equipment through their clamshell rear doors, Soviet Mi-6s await further orders during a 1967 exercise.

specialized attack helicopters retain the capacity to carry a squad of infantry.

Various missions can be undertaken by helicopter-borne raiding parties behind enemy lines. Small teams can be inserted to carry out reconnaissance, direct air strikes and perhaps sabotage enemy equipment. Larger forces may be used to seize and hold a key objective, such as a river crossing or commanding heights, in order to speed up the advance of the main force. The commander of Soviet airborne forces, General D Sukhorukov, has gone so far as to claim that 'vertical envelopment of the enemy has become an important maneuver without which not a single contemporary offensive operation will be possible.' However, helicopter raiding parties will not always operate in direct support of ground forces, as they can be used as an alternative to air strikes to knock out enemy headquarters, airfields, radars, communications equipment and nuclear weapons and delivery systems. These, of course, comprise the overriding priority objectives for all Soviet offensive action.

As a general rule helicopter raiding parties will complement the operations of the parachute troops of the airborne divisions. The latter will usually carry out their raids deep into the enemy rear,

ABOVE: Syrian Mi-8s ferry troops to the top of Mount Harmoun during the 1973 Middle East conflict. Most Arab air arms rely or have relied on Soviet equipment.

Helicopter Strength of Frontal Aviation		
Type	Role	No:
Mi-24 Hind	Attack/assault	800
Mi-8 Hip	Assault	1500
Mi-6 Hook	Heavy Lift	400
Mi-26 Halo	Heavy Lift	?
Mi-4 Hound	Utility	50
Mi-1/2 Hare/Hoplite	Liaison/Scout	700

which is especially useful in delivering fire against enemy forces in contact with friendly troops. Under such conditions it is notoriously difficult for faster-flying, fixed-wing aircraft to distinguish friend from foe. Interestingly enough the US Army's helicopter operations in Vietnam seem to have had a significant influence on Soviet thinking. Soviet articles on the tactical problems of heliborne assaults certainly made reference to the American experience in Vietnam and it is perhaps not a coincidence that in 1967, the year when the AH-1 attack helicopter went into action in Vietnam, the Soviet Air Force experimented with armed helicopters during Exercise Dnepr. However, it is likely that the helicopter's attack mission is regarded as secondary to its trooping duties, as even the Mi-24 Hind-D and E

BELOW: A Mil Mi-4 in flight. Though it resembled a Sikorsky S-55/H-19 in appearance and configuration, it is in fact comparable with the later S-58/H-34 in size and capability.

ALL PICTURES: The Mil design bureau's mighty Mi-26 Halo, the largest operational rotorcraft in the world today. With a cargo hold (FAR RIGHT) comparable to that of a fixed-wing tactical transport, it can accommodate most tanks, field guns or personnel carriers as an alternative to some 100 troops, and is clearly of great value to Soviet forces. Orders for several hundred are expected.

whereas heliborne forces are more likely to make shallower assaults immediately behind the fighting troops. The most attractive targets for attack in the enemy's immediate rear are the logistical support services. Dumps of fuel and ammunition, together with supply convoys moving up to the front, represent soft targets whose destruction will severely hamper the fighting efficiency of front-line troops. Although supply troops will be armed and are trained in the basic combat skills, they are unlikely to be a match for professional infantrymen. The headquarters of higher army formations are particularly attractive targets, as their destruction is likely to dislocate the coordination of the defensive battle. However, because of their importance they are likely to be well guarded. Such destructive raiding in the enemy's rear will have a general usefulness in

lowering enemy morale and in diverting his efforts from the main defensive battle, quite apart from the value of specific targets which can be destroyed.

The all-important attack on enemy nuclear delivery systems and the warhead storage sites is likely to involve a high degree of effort by air-mobile forces. It is quite possible that the Soviet army regards this mission as the primary role of its airborne and air-mobile forces. Certainly, the highly-trained troops of the air-mobile brigades are more likely to be launched against these targets than frittered away in less vital diversionary raids. One of the major problems in dealing with battlefield nuclear systems is in locating them, as their missile and artillery delivery systems are highly mobile. Even when located they will certainly be heavily defended, but the Soviet Army has always been

willing to accept heavy casualties in return for worthwhile results. If Soviet writings on military affairs in their unclassified journals can be believed, the destruction of nuclear weapons is of paramount importance. As with the air interdiction mission, so with heliborne raids or *desants* the permutations of possible objectives are almost endless, while the resources available to carry them out are finite. However, Soviet priorities are likely to be firstly the destruction of nuclear systems, then attacks on headquarters, raids intended to maintain the momentum of the main force's advance and finally disruption and destruction of rear area communications and logistics.

Regarded as a military vehicle for assault transport, the helicopter has definite limitations when compared with the armored personnel carrier. On

ABOVE: The Mi-26 displays its ample cargo-carrying capacity.

the credit side it is considerably more mobile, being able to switch its assaults from sector to sector of the front in a matter of hours, whereas similar movements by motorized units would take days. It is not impeded by obstacles of terrain, such as rivers or mountains (although when operating in 'hot and high' conditions its efficiency is considerably reduced). Lastly helicopters can easily achieve surprise, one of the most cherished of military principles. Attacks can be mounted at short notice and troops landed in a cohesive group near their objectives without giving the enemy any advance warning through the build-up of forces and artillery preparation for the assault. However, helicopters are notoriously vulnerable to enemy fire. It can hardly have escaped the notice of Soviet observers that in Vietnam the Americans lost over 16,000 helicopters when operating for the most part against an enemy equipped only with small arms and heavy machine guns. Furthermore once the heliborne infantrymen is on the ground, he does not have the protection or the fire support of his APC, but must fight with his personal arms on foot. The Soviet Army certainly recognizes this problem and has sought to overcome it in two ways. Firstly it has provided both its attack helicopters and its troop-carrying assault transports with a heavy armament of machine guns and air-to-ground rockets so that they can supply considerable fire support. Secondly, it has deployed heavy lift helicopters with its troop transport regiments so that both artillery and APCs can be flown into the landing zones. These are not likely to be available in the same numbers as those used by standard motor rifle troops, however.

Because of the helicopter's vulnerability to ground fire, special arrangements will have to be made to enable helicopter forces to penetrate front-line air defenses. A number of techniques can be employed to achieve this. Forward enemy anti-

OPPOSITE: A V-2 prototype of the Mi-2 helicopter pictured in 1962. Production of the turbine-powered type took place not in the USSR but in Poland.

aircraft positions can be dealt with by Soviet artillery, provided that their locations have been pinpointed. Suppressive fire can also be laid down by attack helicopters and fixed-wing aircraft. Nap-of-the-earth flying techniques can be used to exploit the protection of terrain masking. This method could be particularly effective if the enemy's defensive positions are sufficiently well known, because modern defenses take the form of fortified bastions rather than continuously defended lines and so evasive routing around them should be practicable. The disadvantage of nap-of-the-earth flying is that it makes it difficult for the helicopter pilots to maintain a cohesive formation. Generally helicopters will fly at a height of 300ft as this offers the best compromise between the needs for terrain masking and formation keeping. Consequently it is only the low-altitude, short-range air defense weapons which are a threat to them. Some attention has been paid in the design of the Mi-24 Hind to providing armored protection for the crew and vital equipment. According to reports from Afghanistan the Hind-D and E attack helicopters are virtually impervious to small arms fire. Although Soviet helicopters do not appear to be fitted with the infra-red suppressors and IR jamming beacons which Western helicopters use, their design does take account of this threat and engine turbine inlet temperatures and exhaust gas temperatures are lower. The Mi-8 Hip troop-carrying helicopter is less well protected than the Hind and all Soviet helicopters are large and noisy machines which can easily be detected by ground observers and radar.

A helicopter assault formation will comprise a main force of troop carrying Mi-8 Hips, escorted by Mi-24 Hinds. The Hinds will form an advance guard and possibly flank guards and will attempt to draw enemy fire and then suppress it before the troop-carrying machines come into range. Similarly the

enemy lines. Mi-8 Hips were used for troop transport and Mi-6 Hooks carried heavy equipment. In the same year Exercise Kavkaz-76 in the Caucasus demonstrated the value of armed attack helicopters in mountainous terrain, where fixed-wing aircraft were often unable to penetrate mountain valleys to deliver ordnance. Helicopters are also useful for scouting and acting as airborne command posts when operating in difficult terrain and the heavy lift types can position artillery on otherwise inaccessible

BELOW: Mil's Mi-4 proved a real workhorse in civil and military guise.

Hinds will lay down fire around the landing zone, possibly following up an initial strike by fixed-wing aircraft. Air cover may also be provided by fighter aircraft to guard against the threat of attack from the air. The West German Luftwaffe has assigned an anti-helicopter role to its Breguet-Dornier Alpha Jet light strike aircraft and troop-carrying helicopters could prove vulnerable to any light fighter or attack aircraft. (This may indeed be a possible role for the Su-25 Frogfoot). A Mi-8 Hip fully loaded with troops and armament has little reserve power available for evasive maneuvering. As all versions of the Hind can carry a squad of eight troops, albeit in some discomfort, they may land advanced teams who will secure and mark the landing zone for the main force. Once the landing zone has been secured the heavy lift Mi-6 Hooks and Mi-26 Halos will fly-in artillery and APCs.

The Soviet forces have frequently employed helicopters during their large-scale maneuvers and these exercises provide some clues as to the progress of their thinking on the role of the battlefield helicopter. In Exercise Dnepr in 1967, the first incidentally in which Soviet forces practiced the techniques of a conventional rather than a nuclear land battle, helicopters were used to spearhead a river crossing under fire. In 1970 during Exercise Dvina widespread use was made of armed helicopters, both as escorts for troop-carrying helicopters and for air attacks on troops and armor. These realistically-conceived exercises evidently provided convincing proof of the usefulness of the attack helicopter on the modern battlefield. By 1976 the heavily-armed Mi-24 Hind had begun to take part in large-scale exercises, two years after it had entered service with the 16th Air Army in East Germany. In Exercise Sever-76 Hinds carried out attacks on armored forces and escorted troop transports on a river-crossing operation and a raid behind

ABOVE: A deadly Mil Mi-24 Hind pictured in typically inhospitable Russian conditions.

BELOW: This Mi-6 being displayed abroad carries two external long-range tanks, the starboard of which is visible inboard of the landing gear.

that a specialized anti-helicopter helicopter (identified as the Mi-28, NATO codename Havoc) is being tested. Its primary target is likely to be Western anti-armor helicopters and their scouts; for just as the Soviet Army has adopted the helicopter as an answer to the problems of maintaining the momentum of the advance, so NATO sees it as an effective means of countering the massive Soviet armored superiority on the Central Front.

Thus the stage is set for treetop-level dogfights between armed helicopters in a future conflict. Existing helicopters could engage in such battles to a limited extent. The Mi-8 Hip, although heavily armed with machine guns and rockets (the latter of very dubious usefulness in air combat), is neither maneuverable enough nor sufficiently well armored to be an effective weapon in helicopter combats. Indeed it is more likely to be cast in the role of the hunted rather than the hunter. In some respects the Mi-24 Hind is better equipped for the role, being both fast and well armored. However, it lacks the rapid acceleration from the hover and the maneuverability that would be required in low-level dogfighting. Another disadvantage is its size and comparatively high profile, which would be a distinct disadvantage in operating from ambush positions. The 'gunship' Hind's main armament is a four-barreled 12.7mm rapid-fire machine gun, which has a rate of fire of more than 4000 rounds per minute and an effective range of around 5000ft. It can be trained to fire at angles of up to 70 degrees off the centerline and can be depressed to an angle of 60 degrees. Although this weapon is likely to be reasonably effective at close ranges, the greater range and hitting power of cannon armament is probably more desirable for the air-to-air role. A 'fire and forget' missile (which will automatically track onto its target after launch) is certainly the best anti-helicopter weapon. An infra-red guided missile, perhaps based on the SA-7 Grail or the heavier AA-8 Aphid, could be developed for this role. Until a specialized anti-helicopter helicopter and arma-

positions. Thus by 1976 Soviet doctrine for the employment of battlefield helicopters had matured and during the remaining years of the decade its forces were rapidly expanded.

With the increasing use of helicopters for battlefield roles rather than for support missions, the development of a specialized anti-helicopter helicopter cannot be far away. The Soviet military theoretician Major General M Belov has written: 'Just as tanks have always been the most effective weapons against tanks, helicopters are the most efficacious means of fighting helicopters. Use of helicopters of both warring sides will inevitably lead to clashes between them. Like tank battles of past wars, a future war between well equipped armies is bound to involve helicopter battles.' Of course any attack helicopter will be able to engage another helicopter and the United States forces clearly expect such actions, as they have armed some of their machines with air-to-air missiles. As yet unconfirmed reports from the Soviet Union suggest

ment are put into service, most actions between helicopters are likely to be unpremeditated brushes between machines intent on other duties.

In contrast to Western armed forces, the Soviet Union apparently does not attach great importance to the helicopter as a scouting vehicle. It is true that some 700 Mi-1 Hare and Mi-2 Hoplite helicopters are available for such miscellaneous duties as liaison, airborne command post and observation. However, these are elderly aircraft, which lack the speed and maneuverability needed for survival in the forward areas of the battlefield. Soviet helicopter designers have yet to produce the small and agile scout helicopter which Western armies appear to find indispensable. This may in part be due to the sheer inability of Soviet industry to produce such a system. It is certainly also a result of differing operational philosophies. Western armies are primarily concerned with defensive operations, and scout helicopters play an important role in their plans for locating and then engaging enemy armored thrusts. The Soviet Army is trained and equipped for offensive operations, in which the cautious probings of scout helicopters can play little part. Furthermore, it is (probably unconsciously) influenced by the nature of the vast plains of Western Russia over which it trains. Scout helicopters will find little natural cover in such terrain and so in Soviet eyes they are machines of limited usefulness, except in such specialized areas as mountain warfare.

The Soviet Army does find that helicopters are useful for artillery observation, although it is necessary for a trained artilleryman to accompany the pilot and spot the fall of shot. Helicopters are thought to be most useful in locating targets during encounter battles, when the artillery often is presented with only a fleeting opportunity to engage. However, helicopters are especially vulnerable under these conditions even if they remain over friendly troop positions. Soviet helicopters have the capability of sowing mines from the air and they have been extensively employed on this duty in

Afghanistan. They will act as airborne command posts and communications relays over their own territory. Specially modified Mi-8s (Hip-J and K) are used as airborne communication jammers and possibly for SIGINT and radar jamming. Another variant of the Mi-8 is apparently used for medical support. However, unlike the United States Army which evacuates its wounded to field hospitals by helicopter, the Soviet Army often adopts the more economical practice of flying its medical teams out to the casualties. Nor are humanitarian concerns of primary importance, as priority treatment will be given to those wounded who can be most speedily returned to service.

Much of the Soviet forces' combat helicopter capability is founded on the capabilities of the Mi-24 Hind. This fast, heavily-armed and rugged helicopter has been in service since 1974 and has been produced in both assault transport and gunship versions. In 1983 there were some 800 Hinds in service

BELOW: The massive Mi-26 in flight, with its impressive eight-bladed main rotor clearly visible in this view.
BOTTOM: Mi-6s in drab military camouflage await their crews on a Soviet airfield.

with Frontal Aviation, 200 of them serving with the five regiments of the Air Forces of the Group of Soviet Forces in Germany. It is believed that a further three regiments of Hinds are serving in Afghanistan. The initial production version of the Mi-24, the Hind-A, can best be described as an assault transport with a secondary attack capability. Its extensively glazed nose section houses a gunner, manning a flexibly-mounted 12.7mm machine gun, with the pilot seated behind him and to the left. A third seat behind is probably for a crew chief, who can carry out routine maintenance on the helicopter when it operates away from base. The fuselage cabin can accommodate a squad of eight troops and their equipment, or ten unencumbered passengers, in cramped conditions. Stub wings are fitted to the fuselage sides, both to offload the main rotor in forward flight and so increase speed and also to provide a mounting for the Hind's heavy weapons load. There are two pylons beneath each wing which usually carry 32-round 57mm rocket pods, but which could also mount cannon pods or bombs. Beneath each wingtip are twin-mountings for AT-2 Swatter anti-tank missiles. These weapons have a maximum range of about 8000ft and can penetrate 20in of armor.

The Hind's fuselage is a well-streamlined shape and, unusually for a helicopter, it is fitted with a retractable undercarriage. Speed clearly was one of the design priorities. Early Hinds were powered by twin 1500shp Isotov TV-2 turboshafts, the same powerplant as that fitted to the Mi-8 Hip. Later production helicopters have the more powerful TV-3 turboshafts, which are rated at 2200shp. The five-bladed main rotor has a 55ft 9in diameter and an aerofoil section optimized for high-speed flight. Maximum speed is estimated to be 215mph, but this will be reduced when underwing ordnance is carried. Cruising speed is around 150mph and combat

BELOW: Mi-8 helicopters in Egypt. Although once heavily dependent on Soviet military support, Egypt has latterly turned West for equipment.

radius with a full weapons load is 160 miles. The Hind's excellent high-speed performance is not matched by its acceleration from the hover or its maneuverability. Therefore it is most unlikely to be used in the same way as Western anti-armor and attack helicopters, which operate from behind cover and pop up only briefly to engage their targets. With its high speed and heavy armament, the Hind will seek to encounter opposition head-on rather than try to evade it.

The first significant modification to the Mi-24 design came with the Hind-D (the Hind-B and C designations being given to an experimental prototype and a training version respectively). This version was primarily intended for the attack mission, with the front fuselage entirely redesigned to accommodate the pilot and gunner in individual cockpits. The visibility from the Hind-A's cockpit was somewhat limited by the framing, but the individual balloon-shaped cockpit canopies of the Hind-D are a considerable improvement. The gun armament of the D has been improved by substituting a four-barrel 12.7mm machine gun, mounted in a remotely-operated, trainable turret beneath the nose, for the gunner's hand-held weapon of the Hind-A. Apart from this, the armament is unchanged. However, the Hind-D is fitted with a new range of target acquisition and tracking sensors which are likely to improve the accuracy of weapons delivery to a considerable degree. They include a magnified optical site for target tracking, perhaps making use of low-light TV for operations at night; a laser rangefinder; and a low-speed air data sensor which probably feeds information to a simple weapons aiming computer. The Hind-D retains the capability of lifting an infantry squad, but in practice it most often operates in the attack role. Some observers have seen in the attack version of the Hind a successor to the Il-2 Shturmovik, having a close air support and anti-tank role in support of armored forces. This is certainly one aspect of its capabilities, but it is a rather more flexible weapons system and will certainly undertake helicopter escort missions and most probably be used in the secondary roles of assault transport, anti-helicopter and defense suppression (particularly of NATO anti-tank missile teams).

Various improvements to the Mi-24's armament have been noted since the appearance of the Hind-D. The anti-tank missiles carried by the Hind-E are improved AT-6 Spirals. These are tube-launched weapons, which have a range of 16,000ft and a greater armor-penetrative capability in comparison with Swatter. In 1982 a number of Hind-Es fitted with a fixed, twin-barrel 23mm cannon were shown to Western military observers during the Warsaw Pact exercise Druzhba-82. This installation was mounted on the starboard side of the fuselage and the turret-mounted machine gun was deleted. This version may have been given the NATO reporting name Hind-F, but it is probably not in widespread use. The fixed cannon may be intended as an anti-helicopter weapon, or may simply reflect dissatisfaction with the 12.7mm armament. It is probable that future developments of the Hind will include a version armed with a 23mm multi-barrel cannon in the nose turret.

The standard troop transport helicopter in Frontal Aviation service is the Mi-8 Hip. It is an effective medium range, all-weather helicopter with a ruggedness and reliability which suits it equally well for the assault transport role or for civil

development work in remote parts of the Soviet Union. Therefore the 1500 Mi-8s in military service could be rapidly augmented by a considerable number withdrawn from Aeroflot in time of emergency. Great attention has been paid to ease of maintenance in the Mi-8's design, to ensure that routine work is kept to the barest minimum and that those components which do require regular attention are easily accessible. Indeed Mikhail Mil, the helicopter's chief designer, aptly summarized the philosophy of all Soviet engineers who build military hardware when he wrote: 'Make it simple, make it cheap and make it work.' Hips have fulfilled this injunction from the deserts of Somalia up to the frozen tundra of the Soviet Arctic.

The Hip can lift a maximum of 28 fully equipped troops, although this load will probably be halved if the helicopter carries maximum fuel and full armament. Unlike the US Army's assault helicopters which are tailored around the infantry squad of eleven men, the Mi-8 is intended to lift the greatest number of troops possible within its weight limitations. The Mi-8 also has a useful secondary cargo-carrying capability, as it can lift an 8800lb payload and its rear-loading clamshell doors allow small vehicles to be carried. Fuel tanks are mounted externally on the fuselage sides to enable the maximum amount of cabin space to be used for cargo, at some penalty in vulnerability to groundfire. The Hip can also lift underslung loads of up to 6400lb in weight. Two pilots are accommodated in the nose section and a crew chief sits behind them. When it is

ABOVE: The versatile Mi-8 may be employed as an air ambulance, such as the pictured example in the service of the Yugoslav forces.

LEFT: The ultimate in air/ground operations? An Mi-2 and a Warsaw Pact tank demonstrate the art.

used in the casualty evacuation role, twelve stretcher patients are carried.

The Mi-8 is powered by two 1500shp Isotov TV-2 turboshafts mounted above the fuselage cabin and driving a five-bladed main rotor. Maximum speed is 143mph and range is 265 miles with a 6500lb payload. Late production Mi-8s are fitted with more powerful TV-3 turboshafts and a transmission system similar to that of the naval Mi-14 Haze. These helicopters have been given the NATO reporting name Hip-H and the Soviet designation is believed to be Mi-17. The basic assault transport variant, the Hip-C, is armed with four 32-round 57mm rocket pods, carried on outriggers on the fuselage sides. These weapons are used to suppress groundfire during assault landings, as with its limited maneuverability at full payload the Hip is of little use as an attack helicopter. Nonetheless, the Hip-E version carries an even heavier armament, comprising six 32-round rocket pods and four AT-2 Swatter anti-tank missiles carried on the outriggers and a nose-mounted 12.7mm machine gun. Additional fire can be provided by the troops' personal weapons. This heavy armament probably reflects Soviet worries that helicopter-borne raiding parties may have insufficient fire support after landing. During the Yom Kippur War of 1973 Egyptian commandos were carried behind enemy lines by

BELOW: The twin Lotarev engines and massive rotor hub of the Mi-26. The latter is fashioned in titanium to save weight – and, while the rotor itself is smaller in diameter than that of the Mi-6 and Mi-10, the end result was a helicopter with an empty weight of less than half its maximum take-off weight.

Mi-8s, which then provided them with fire support. Ideally this role would be undertaken by Hind-D/E attack helicopters, but Soviet commanders are hard-headed enough to realize that such specialized machines will not always be available.

In the Soviet view one of the best ways of ensuring that raiding forces are provided with adequate fire-support is to fly artillery and armored vehicles into the landing zones. Hence the Soviet interest in heavy-lift helicopters which has produced in the Mi-26 Halo the largest machine of its kind in the world. With a maximum take-off weight of 123,500 lb, the Mi-26 can carry a payload of 44,000lb. Power is provided by two 11,400shp Lotarev D-136 turbo-shafts, giving a maximum speed of 183mph and a range of some 500 miles. The helicopter's capacious cargo hold is much the same size as that of a fixed-wing tactical transport, such as the An-12 or Lockheed C-130 Hercules. It can accommodate more than 100 combat-equipped infantrymen, but will more usually be used for equipment. Possible internal loads include the PT-76 amphibious tank, BMD and BMP armored personnel carriers and the ZSU-23-4 tracked AA gun. Artillery pieces will be carried as underslung loads. Only the large 180mm S-23 field gun is heavier than the Mi-26's 44,000lb payload and even this weapon may be lifted by helicopters operating in overload conditions. However, a more useful load would be one of the lighter 152mm, 130mm or 122mm pieces, together with its crew and an initial supply of ammunition. The Mi-26 would also be invaluable as a flying crane to support military engineering work, and to recover damaged helicopters and armored vehicles for repair. However, only a handful were in Soviet service at the end of 1983, although several hundred may be supplied to Frontal Aviation in the coming decade to replace the Mi-6 Hook.

The 400 Mi-6s which currently undertake the heavy-lift mission are themselves massive machines, which were for many years the largest helicopters in service. The Mi-6 is powered by two 5500shp Soloviev D-25V turboshafts and has a maximum weight for vertical take-off of 93,700lb. If it makes a rolling take-off during which its detachable stub wings give increased lift, then this weight can be exceeded. Up to 26,500lb loads can be carried in the cabin, or 17,600lb can be underslung on the cargo hook. Maximum speed is 186mph and range carrying two-thirds of the maximum payload is 385 miles. Typical loads for the Mi-6 include heavy artillery, surface-to-air missiles, FROG artillery rockets, PT-76 tanks and armored personnel carriers. It was General Petrov's Mi-6s which lifted PT-76 tanks and armored personnel carriers over the mountains during the course of the battle for Jijiga in the Ogaden War in 1978.

The least impressive of all Soviet military helicopters are the scouting/liaison types. The Mi-1 Hare is a piston-engined machine with a maximum speed of 125mph and a range of 205 miles. It can accommodate a pilot and up to three passengers. The type has been in Soviet military service since 1951 and as production ended in the mid 1960s the survivors are now long overdue for replacement. The Mi-2 Hoplite is a turbine-powered development of the Mi-1 with twice that helicopter's passenger capacity. Although designed in the Soviet Union, all production has been undertaken by PZL in Poland and over 3000 have been built. Maximum speed is 130mph and range is just over 100 miles. The large Mi-4 of 1952 is similar in lay-out to the now-obsolete American Sikorsky H-19 and was employed in the 1950s and 1960s as a 12-seat troop transport. The 50 or so survivors probably serve as liaison transport and command posts. A number have seen service in Afghanistan.

Although the Soviet Army as been slow to appreciate the role of the helicopter on the modern battlefield, its present capabilities are formidable. Helicopter forces can be used in swift and unexpected assaults throughout the depth of the enemy's defenses in accordance with the classic Soviet principles of war. Consequently they are likely to make a decisive contribution to the success of Soviet arms in the land battle.

CHAPTER SEVEN

AIR TRANSPORT AND TRAINING

The Soviet Air Force's Military Transport Aviation (VTA, or *Voenno-transportnaya aviatsiya*) is in some respects the poor relation among the air commands. With a personnel strength of some 50,000 it is smaller even than the Naval Air Force. There are some 600 medium and long-range transport aircraft in service. However, numbers of aircraft can by themselves be a misleading yardstick, as although the number of transports in the Military Transport Aviation inventory has dropped by around 60 during the past five years, the command's airlift capacity has risen by an impressive 50 percent. Nonetheless it would be idle to deny that the Soviet requirement for military airlift capacity is far less important than is that of the United States. This is of course largely due to geographical factors, as the Soviet Union's central position within the Eurasian landmass facilitates the movement of its military forces to a far greater degree. In order to reinforce Europe or the Western Pacific the United States has to cross a substantial ocean barrier, whereas the Soviet Union can make use of well-established land lines of communication.

This is not to suggest that Soviet Union does not have a valid operational mission for its air transport forces, but rather that they do not occupy the key position of the USAF's Military Airlift Command. In order for the United States to mount a credible defense of its interests in Europe, the Middle East and the Western Pacific, it must be capable of rapid reinforcement by air. The Soviet Union already has substantial forces deployed within her vast territories which could rapidly intervene in any of these strategically important areas. It is true that air transport will allow forces to be switched from one theater to another with far greater speed than is possible by land communications and this strategic reinforcement role is important. Although the Soviet Army is a vast organization numbering 184 tank and motor rifle divisions, not all these units are maintained at peak readiness. Many of them in the interior military districts are cadre formations which will require an infusion of men and equipment to bring them to a state of combat readiness. If they are

then to reach the combat theater in time to influence what Soviet plans intend shall be a short war, they will require air transportation. It has been estimated that it will take five days for a division to travel from the Western Soviet Union to the West German border by land and so clearly any reinforcements from further afield will benefit considerably from air transport. It is not only troop reinforcements and their equipment that need to be fed rapidly into the battle area, however. The combat experience of the Arab-Israeli Yom Kippur War of 1973 showed that modern forces will expend ordnance at a prodigious rate and this suggests that the speedy resupply of munitions will be essential if Soviet forces are to maintain a high speed of advance. Air transport is especially suited to this task as it is able to move these supplies from rear area depots to the combat area within hours and if necessary parachute them directly to units in the field.

The Yom Kippur War illustrated another aspect of the operations of Military Transport Aviation, for just as the United States was forced to mount an emergency airlift to resupply Israel, so the Soviet Union had to fly urgently-needed equipment to Egypt and Syria. As a superpower, the Soviet Union's interests are not confined to its own border areas, but are worldwide. Therefore airlift operations are an important part of Soviet global power projection capability. During the civil war in Angola during 1975-76, Military Transport Aviation's Il-76 Candid and An-22 Cock transports flew airlift missions within the country in support of MPLA forces. Civil Il-62 passenger transports of the

Soviet national airline Aeroflot were used to carry troop reinforcements from Cuba into the country at a decisive stage of the war in early 1976 and the continuing Cuban military presence in Angola is supported by Soviet military transport aircraft. Incidentally the close links between Military Transport Aviation and Aeroflot are very useful in supporting operations of this kind as a civil airliner will find it much easier to obtain landing clearances and permission for overflights en route than will a military transport. Apart from their civil livery and registrations, Aeroflot's An-12 and Il-76 transport aircraft are indistinguishable from their military counterparts – even retaining the former's tail gun positions, although armament is of course not fitted. Military Transport Aviation was also active in supporting the Soviet and Cuban military forces in Ethiopia during the Ogaden War of 1978 and some 200 daily flights were made from the Soviet Union to Addis Ababa before the counteroffensive was launched against Jijiga.

One further instructive illustration of Soviet military airlift doctrine can be drawn from the Yom Kippur War. At the point in late October 1973 when it was feared that Israel would break the cease-fire agreement and continue its advance into Egypt, the Soviet transport aircraft were switched from their cargo flights and concentrated on airfields adjacent to the airborne forces' garrisons. The Soviet threat to intervene was sufficient to gain Israel's compliance with the ceasefire. However, the incident does highlight the fact that the Soviet Union has a considerable force of airborne troops, currently numbering seven divisions. This force is not of course primarily an international fire-brigade and the nearest that the Soviet Army has ever come to using it in such a role was during the occupation of Czechoslovakia in 1968. It is rather a large scale raiding force for operations in enemy rear areas

BELOW: Despite its civil registration, this Il-76's tail turret – though no gun – is clearly visible.

during a major war. Unlike the air-mobile brigades which are assigned to theater commanders, the airborne divisions are directly controlled by the Soviet High Command. This reflects the considerable importance that the General Staff attaches to their employment, as the position of the airborne divisions in the Soviet chain of command is virtually that of an independent service.

With an individual strength of between 7000 and 8000 men, each airborne division is a powerful self-contained force, which is made up of three parachute assault regiments equipped with BMD air-portable armored personnel carriers, together with support troops. The latter includes a divisional artillery regiment, reconnaissance, engineer, signals and chemical defense troops. An eighth airborne division serves with the Polish Army. If several of

nerable to counter-attack. The final deciding factor on determining the strength of airborne assaults is likely to be availability of aircraft. The airborne divisions will certainly not enjoy an absolute priority in the allocation of transport aircraft, as many will be needed for reinforcement and resupply duties. Whatever the strength of the airborne force, it will be essential for the operation to be well coordinated with that of the main armies, because unless they are reinforced within a matter of days they will be unable to survive. Some objectives of course may be considered worth the loss of an airborne division by the Soviet High Command. Even if airlift is not available for all seven divisions, they will be useful as a special strategic reserve. During the Great Patriotic War most airborne soldiers fought as infantrymen rather than as paratroops.

BELOW: An Antonov An-12 transport stages through Keflavik in Iceland, where Western and Soviet types stand side-by-side on the tarmac. Note the US Navy P-3 Orions in the background.

these divisions were grouped together they would form a powerful airborne army; however it is unlikely that sufficient transport aircraft could be assembled in wartime to lift more than a single division at a time. One possibility would be for an airborne force to capture an airfield behind enemy lines into which substantial reinforcements could be flown. The back-up units of course need not be trained paratroops. This operational plan was used in Czechoslovakia in 1968 and has been exercised during maneuvers. However, it is not typical of airborne operations. These are essentially diversions planned in concert with a ground offensive; for airborne landings are, in the words of a former Soviet airborne forces commander, 'operations in coordination with the main arms of the ground forces so as to ensure the high speed and continuity of the offensive.'

It may well be that parachute assaults will usually be made in regimental rather than divisional strength. Large airborne drops are difficult operations to coordinate and if the forces become scattered on the ground they will be extremely vul-

The military air transport reserve provided by the Soviet state airline Aeroflot is in many ways more efficient than that of the United States' Civil Reserve Air Fleet. In the first place all Soviet civil air transports are under the airline's control and can be readily diverted to military use. The airline's director is a military officer, Marshal of Aviation P B Buguayev, and all its aircrew are Air Force reservists. Furthermore, 200 of the airline's civil fleet are Il-76 Candid and An-12 Cub transports designed specifically for the military airlift mission. About half of the 110 or so An-22 Cock heavy-lift transports built were supplied to Aeroflot and these are equipped to the same standard as the remainder which serve with Military Transport Aviation. In peacetime they are used mainly to support civil construction projects in the Siberian wastelands, but they can double the Air Force's heavy lift capability literally overnight. The 1200 medium and long-haul passenger transports which serve Aeroflot's 500,000 miles of civil air routes have only a limited cargo capacity. However, they will be useful in carrying out trooping flights within the Soviet Union during the mobilization of reserves, thus releasing military transports for more warlike missions. In order to achieve the maximum surprise, the mobilization of reserve forces will probably occur only after the opening of hostilities.

Aeroflot's international flights may be used to deploy units of the GRU's *Spetsnaz* forces abroad under cover of normal civil air operations on the eve of hostilities. These special force troops will operate against the usual range of interdiction targets (nuclear weapons, command centers, airfields etc), perform acts of sabotage against civil power stations, oil and gas storage sites, and seek to assassinate key civil and military leaders. All *Spetsnaz* troops are trained parachutists and will be dropped into enemy territory by Military Transport Aviation in wartime, or more rarely carried by helicopter. Night paradrops are preferred because they are less conspicuous than a helicopter landing. It is probable that a number of air transport regiments specialize in low altitude delivery techniques, as do the MC-130E-

equipped Special Operations Squadrons of the US Air Force.

The standard paratroop transport in Military Transport Aviation service is the Il-76 Candid. It is able to lift a company of paratroopers together with such artillery support pieces as the 122mm towed field howitzer and their tractors over a range of 3100 miles. During Exercise Berezina, which was held in Byelorussia in February 1978, Il-76s dropped a force of 1300 paratroopers together with 27 vehicles into a

ABOVE: An An-12's tail turret reflects the type's military purpose.
BELOW: The An-10 is an airliner version of the original design which spawned the An-12. Broadly similar in configuration, it lacks its sister's tail loading ramp.

ABOVE: The high wing and tailplane of the Ilyushin Il-76, together with its remarkably short take-off and landing run, suits it for operations from rough, unprepared airfields.

drop zone measuring 3000ft by 16,000ft within the space of 20 minutes. The drop was made from a height of 2400ft with the transports flying at a speed of 140 knots. Various palletized and container systems are used to drop vehicles and supplies. A BMD APC or howitzer is fastened to a pallet, which is pulled from the aircraft's cargo hold by a drogue parachute. The load is then lowered to the ground beneath a cluster of three or five main parachutes. Just before the pallet and its load reaches the ground, a group of retro rockets is fired to slow its descent so that its impact with the ground is very gentle. A slow rate of descent is generally undesirable for air-dropped loads, in the Soviet view, because the load tends to drift away from the drop zone and the longer it is in the air the more vulnerable it is to groundfire. The standard 1100lb cargo pallet load descends under its parachute at a rate of 48ft per second, but much of its heavy impact is absorbed by the pallet which is padded by layers of paper honeycomb. Fuel is dropped in a robustly-constructed metal container with a capacity of 44 gallons of liquid. Other supplies such as ammunition, rations, medical stores etc are packed into small metal containers, each of which takes a 220lb load. A small auxiliary parachute lowers the container at a high rate of descent until it nears the ground and a large braking chute deploys.

In many cases Soviet transports will land to unload their cargoes during resupply missions. It is even likely that airheads will be established in the enemy's rear by air assault forces or operational maneuver groups, so that tactical transports can fly

in supplies and reinforcements and evacuate casualties. These need not necessarily be well-equipped permanent airfields captured from the enemy. Soviet transport aircraft are generally designed with rugged undercarriages and low-pressure tires and so are quite capable of operating from unsurfaced airstrips. This design philosophy extends even to the massive An-22 Cock heavy-lift freighter, which has an excellent rough-field capability enabling it to fly such outsize loads as main battle tanks and SA-4 missiles on their twin-round tracked launcher into unsurfaced forward airstrips. A corollary to this rough-field capability is the Soviet transport aircraft's ability to function without ground support equipment. Soviet transports are invariably fitted with an auxiliary power unit so that their engines can be started without using an external power supply. They incorporate on-board self-testing equipment, which allows technical faults to be readily identified and dealt with by the flight engineer. Refueling is accomplished by a single-point system which can either use pressure refueling, if available, for a quick turnaround, or use gravity feed. Cargo can be unloaded by using an overhead hoist fitted to the roof of the freight hold, or by chain conveyors incorporated into the floor. Thus any load can be transferred to a standard truck without the need for any kind of specialized cargo-handling equipment.

The most modern transport aircraft in service with the Soviet regiments is the Il-76 Candid. This aircraft combines the strategic airlift capability of the American C-141 Starlifter (which it somewhat resembles) with the ability of the tactical transport to operate from short, unprepared landing strips. It can thus pick up reinforcements and supplies from airfields in the interior of the Soviet Union and fly them right into the battle zone. This eliminates the need to land at a forward airhead and transfer the load to a tactical transport aircraft for onward shipment to the armies in the field. Quite apart from its valuable dual role as an intertheater and tactical transport, the Il-76 is a far more capable aircraft than the An-12 Cub which it is gradually replacing in Military Transport Aviation service. Not only is the Il-76 much faster, but it is able to carry twice the An-12's maximum payload over distances greater than the latter's maximum range. When it is required to air-drop supplies, the Il-76 can lift 40 standard pallet loads to the An-12's 34 and double the number of 220lb-load containers that the An-12 can handle (280 compared with 140). The Il-76 is also better able to support the operations of airborne forces, as not only is the number of paratroopers

dropped from one aircraft increased from 65 to 120, but they can be lifted both farther and faster. With fewer transport aircraft involved in the tactical drop of an airborne division, the soldiers and their equipment can be landed more quickly and in a more compact formation and will thus be ready for combat in full strength so much the sooner. It is significant that in recent large scale Soviet exercises, airborne forces have invariably been carried by Il-76s, even though the process of phasing out the An-12 has barely begun. At the end of 1983 there were 175 Il-76s in service, compared with 375 An-12s.

The Il-76 is powered by four 26,500lb thrust Soloviev D-30KP turbofans, mounted in nacelles beneath the high-mounted wing. Soviet turbofans are notoriously less efficient than those produced in the West and the Il-86 wide-bodied airliner has suffered considerable development problems through inadequate power. Nonetheless, the Il-76 has achieved a basic capability of transporting a 88,000lb maximum payload over a distance of 3100 miles within a period of six hours. In practice it has been found that an increased range with reduced payload is more desirable and the limited fuel capacity of early production Il-76s was increased by some 20 percent on subsequent aircraft to a maximum of 18,000 gallons (adding 1000 miles to the maximum range). The 165ft 8in span wing is fitted with double-slotted trailing edge flaps in order to improve low speed performance and overwing spoilers are used rather than the small ailerons for roll control at these speeds. These are needed when the aircraft is operating into short airstrips; landings can be made within 1500ft, while take-offs require almost double that distance. The Il-76's maximum take-off weight is 375,000lb, but aircraft operating from unsurfaced forward airstrips will be more lightly loaded. The rough-field landing gear comprises no fewer than 20

Aircraft Strength of Military Transport Aviation		
Type	**Role**	**No:**
Il-76 Candid	Tac Transport	175
An-12 Cub	Tac Transport	375
An-22 Cock	Heavy Transport	55
Il-18 Coot	Troop Transport	30
Il-14 Crate	Utility Transport	25
An-26 Curl	Utility Transport	50
An-2 Colt	Utility Transport	500
Il-62 Classic	VIP Transport	3
Tu-134 Crusty	VIP Transport	8
Tu-154 Careless	VIP Transport	5
Yak-40 Codling	VIP Transport	20

BELOW: A mechanical digger is swallowed up in the Antonov An-22's cavernous hold. Many of these aircraft find employment in Siberia, where they support civil construction work, but can double the air force's heavy lift capability if and when required.

wheels, with each main unit comprising four pairs and the nose unit two pairs.

The circular-section cargo-hold measures 11ft 4in wide and 11ft 2in high and is 65ft 7in long. Loading is facilitated by a rear-mounted cargo ramp, which can be lowered in flight for air drops. The normal operating crew comprises seven members, made up of the aircraft captain and co-pilot, flight engineer, navigator, radio operator, loadmaster and tail gunner. The navigator occupies a nose compartment which has observation windows for use during cargo or paratroop drops. The gunner is provided with twin 23mm cannon and a tail-warning and ranging radar. This armament provides a limited rearward defense in the event of fighter interception, although it would be easily outranged even by short-range AAMs. It might also prove useful against ground targets of opportunity during low-level missions. In general, Soviet bomber and transport aircraft carry a defensive cannon armament, whereas most Western air forces have long ago abandoned the practice. Even if its practical usefulness is small, it is likely to have a beneficial effect on the morale of Soviet aircrews. Production of the Il-76 is comparatively slow and only some 30 aircraft are supplied to the Soviet Air Force each year. The Candid design has been adapted for the airborne warning and control role as the Mainstay and a tanker version is also being developed.

Because of the slow rate of Il-76 deliveries, the An-12 Cub is likely to remain in widespread service with Military Transport Aviation until well into the 1990s. This four-turboprop, high-wing transport is

the Soviet equivalent of the USAF's C-130 Hercules, although it has not been produced in the same numbers, nor does it carry out as great a variety of operational roles as the American aircraft. The basic transport version of the An-12 is known as Cub-A by NATO. Cub-B is an ELINT variant which serves with the Naval Air Force and Cub-C is equipped for electronic countermeasures. It is believed that another version has been modified as an airborne command post. Production of the An-12 ended in 1973 after around 850 examples had been produced. The An-12 is powered by four 4000shp Ivchenko AI-20K turboprops, which gave a cruising speed of 360mph. The maximum payload is 44,000lb, but to achieve a range of 2100 miles this load has to be halved. Range with maximum fuel is 3500 miles. Maximum take-off weight is 134,500lb and the An-12 requires only 2800ft of runway for its take-off run. Like all Soviet military transport aircraft, it can operate from rough airstrips.

The An-12's cargo hold measures 11ft 5in across, 8ft 6in high and is 43ft long. This is sufficient to accommodate eight 5500lb cargo pallets, 100 infantrymen or 65 parachutists. There is a rear-loading cargo ramp, which can be lowered in flight for air drops. The aircraft's service ceiling is 33,500ft. Like the Il-76, the An-12 is fitted with a tail gun position armed with twin 23mm cannon, but no ranging radar is fitted. The navigator, however, does have a weather and ground-mapping radar which is fitted beneath his glazed nose observation position.

A typical vehicle load for the An-12 and Il-76 transports would be the airborne divisions' BMD

BELOW: An An-22 touches down. Despite being superseded by the US C-5 Galaxy as the world's largest aircraft. the type is still extremely impressive.

armored personnel carriers, ASU-85 assault guns or 122mm D-30 field howitzers. However, a heavier airlift capability is needed for the air reinforcement role, or for air landing operations when an airfield is captured behind enemy lines. This is at present provided by the massive An-22 Cock, which was the world's largest aircraft until the appearance of the USAF's C-5A Galaxy in 1968. An An-22 can accommodate such loads as a pair of SA-4 Ganef SAMs on their tracked launcher, T-72 main battle tanks and battlefield surface-to-surface missiles. Its maximum payload is 175,000lb and the cargo hold is 14ft 5in square in section and 108ft in length. At its maximum take-off weight of 550,000lb, the An-22 will leave the ground after a 5000ft take-off run. A rear fuselage cargo loading ramp is fitted, but though the An-22 is not used for air-dropping loads, it can land on unsurfaced airstrips to offload its cargo.

The An-22 is powered by four 15,000shp Kuznetsov NK-12MV turboprops driving massive 20ft 4in diameter contra-rotating propellers. These provide sufficient airflow over the wing surfaces and flaps during a landing approach to substitute for a more conventional 'blown flap' system and make an important contribution to this massive aircraft's excellent short-field performance. The undercarriage comprises three twin-wheel main units mounted in blisters on each side of the fuselage and a twin nosewheel unit, all fitted with massive, low-pressure tires for good rough-field operation. The An-22's range and payload characteristics are equally impressive, as it can cover 6800 miles carrying 100,000lb of cargo. The An-22 is indeed unique in combining

ABOVE: Final approach of the curiously configured Antonov An-72. Exhaust gases from its twin turbofans blown over the wing trailing edge confer a good short take-off and landing capability.

ABOVE: The An-32 differs from the similar An-26 in having more powerful engines.

the range and payload of a strategic transport with the field performance of a tactical transport. However, there is some doubt as to the type's safety and reliability, as three An-22s are known to have crashed outside the Soviet Union and other accidents within Soviet territory may well have occurred. The aircraft's cruising speed is particularly low at 320mph, compared with a comparable value of 537mph for the American C-5A Galaxy. Consequently the An-22's remarkable operational flexibility has only been achieved by accepting severe penalties in performance and, perhaps, at the expense of reliability.

A new heavyweight strategic military freighter is reported to be at an advanced stage of development and will probably enter service with Military Transport Aviation in the late 1980s. It is a product of the Antonov design bureau and has been variously identified as the An-40 and An-400. NATO has given the aircraft the reporting name of Condor, an indication that it expects it to progress from experimental to service status. It is a turbofan powered aircraft, resembling in plan-view a scaled-up Boeing 747 and will regain for the Soviet Union the distinction (of dubious value) of possessing the world's largest aircraft. It is believed to have a maximum payload of 264,000lb, which it will be able to lift over a range of 2800 miles. It will certainly be able to accommodate all of the Soviet Army's combat vehicles and artillery pieces and may well have the capability of transporting the SS-20 missile system between theaters. If it is used as a troop transport, up to 200 infantrymen or paratroopers could be carried. It is inconceivable that such an aircraft would have the same capability as the An-22 to operate from tactical airstrips. Therefore its main role is likely to be intertheater reinforcement and logistical support. It may well also reflect a growing Soviet interest in worldwide power projection.

The Soviet Air Force has three classifications for its transport operations: strategic transport, operational-tactical transport and tactical transport. The An-22 falls into the first category, the Il-76 can perform both strategic and operational-tactical missions, while the An-12 is almost exclusively concerned with the latter. Tactical transports in the Soviet classification are short-range aircraft such as the An-26 Curl and An-2 Colt. They will operate not as the strategic and operational-tactical transports do in the independent regiments of Military Transport Aviation, but will rather be attached to the tactical divisions of Frontal Aviation in squadron strength. They provide the air forces of each military district with a limited air transport force for short-range communications, cargo, personnel and VIP transport work.

The An-26 Curl is a military transport developed from the An-24 twin-turboprop, short-haul airliner. The principal change was the fitting of a rear-loading cargo ramp, plus winch and conveyor system for cargo handling. The An-32 has more powerful turboprops, while the An-30 is a combined freighter and photographic survey aircraft. More than fifty aircraft of this family are in Soviet military service. The basic An-26 military transport has a cruising speed of 270mph and can lift a 12,000lb payload (or

50 passengers) over a range of 560 miles. The robust and workmanlike An-2 Colt utility transport biplane is still in widespread service, with more than 500 in the Soviet Air Force inventory – despite the age of the design, which was conceived immediately after World War II and first took to the air in 1947. With a payload of 2850lb or 14 passengers, the An-2 cruises at around 110mph over a range of 525 miles. It is able to operate from a 600ft airstrip, making it the ideal utility transport for theater operations. In the fast-changing world of aviation technology, it is the illustration *par excellence* of the Soviet predilection for keeping in service any system which has a vestige of remaining usefulness.

If no replacement is in sight for the An-2, the 1960s-vintage An-26 may be superseded by the An-72 Coaler in the mid 1980s. Although it is thought to be in production, it is at present unclear whether any examples of the Coaler have yet entered military service. The An-72 is powered by two 14,300lb thrust turbofans which are mounted high on the wing, so that exhaust gasses (which are comparatively cool with a high bypass turbofan) are blown over the wing trailing edge to increase lift. This technique gives the An-72 excellent low-speed handling characteristics, which combine with a maximum payload of 16,500lb or 24 passengers to

BELOW: Antonov's An-72 may well replace some of the bureau's twin-turboprop transports in military service as the 1980s progress. This early example is pictured in Aeroflot service.

BELOW: A Hungarian-registered example of the An-2 utility biplane. Although antiquated in appearance, the type still provides Frontal Aviation with short-range transport and communications.

produce a useful military STOL (short take-off and landing) transport.

A number of civil air transport designs serve with the Soviet Air Force in small numbers. The thirty-or-so surviving Il-14 Crates, twin piston-engined airliners which can carry a maximum payload of 7300lb over 250 miles, are probably now relegated to the air forces of the less important military districts as short-range cargo transports. The same

number of Il-18 Coots, four-turboprop airliners which can carry 80 to 120 passengers over a range of 4000 miles, are more useful for trooping flights. Each year newly-trained conscripts are flown to East Germany to join units of the GSFG, while time-expired troops are returned to the Soviet Union in a single large airlift. A similar operation could very quickly bring Category 2 army divisions (with a peacetime strength of 75 percent of the necessary

RIGHT: The glazed nose of this An-30 betrays its dual freight and photo survey role.

133

OPPOSITE: The production line of An-26 transports in the mid 1960s.

TOP: Derived from the An-24 airliner, the An-26's rear loading ramp enables bulky freight loads to be carried.

ABOVE: The An-26 series superseded the earlier piston-engined Ilyushin transports typified by this Il-14 in the colors of the East German air force.

LEFT: The ubiquitous Antonov An-2 biplane.

personnel) up to full strength. More modern airliners are used as VIP transports for senior government and party officials. They include long-range Il-62, medium-range Tu-134s and Tu-154s, and short-haul Yak-40s.

The training of military aircrew is the responsibility of the Air Force Deputy Commander for Schools and Academies, who controls a force of some 1000 fixed-wing trainers and 700 helicopters. He provides fully-trained pilots and navigators for service with the Aviation Armies of the Soviet Union, Frontal Aviation, Military Transport Aviation and the Naval Air Force. The Air Defense Forces has its own training organization. Pre-service flying training on powered aircraft and gliders is provided by the para-military DOSAAF (*Dobrovol'*

LEFT: A Polish Air Force Ilyushin Il-18. More often seen in airline livery, the type also serves as a military troop transport.

BELOW: The Ilyushin Il-62 serves in the same troop-carrying role as did its RAF counterpart, the VC10.

RIGHT: Training variants of Soviet combat types are always denoted by the U-suffix after the designation. This is a Finnish MiG-21U.

LEFT: Yakovlev's diminutive Yak-40 is among the civil types pressed into military service as short-range VIP transports.

RIGHT: The adoption of the turbofan-powered Aero L-39 Albatros as the standard Soviet jet trainer was unusual indeed, since the type is designed and built in Czechoslovakia. A maker's demonstration aircraft is pictured.

ABOVE: A Scud rocket on a tank chassis is loaded into the gaping hold of an An-22.

noe obshchestvo sodeistviya Armii, Aviatsii i Flotu, or Voluntary Society for the support of the Army, Aviation and the Fleet). Basic and advanced flying training is carried out by the various Air Force schools. These include the Barnaul Higher Air Force School (HAFS), the Tambov Raskova HAFS, the Syzran HAFS, the Orenburg Polbin HAFS, the Saratov HAFS, the Chernigov Lenin Komsomol HAFS, the Balashov HAFS, the Borisoglebsk HAFS, the Gritsevets HAFS, the Yeisk Komarov HASF, the Armavir HAFS and Kacha Myasnikov HASF. Many of the schools in the vast flying training organization are located in the southern Soviet Union to take advantage of the better weather. As well as the pilot training aca-

demies, there are specialist schools for navigators and numerous Air Force Technical Schools. The Air Defense Forces training organization includes schools for pilots, navigators, SAM crews and electronic specialists. Air Force higher military education is the responsibility of the Gagarin Red Banner Air Force Academy, situated at Monino near Moscow.

Basic flying training is conducted on the Yak-18 piston-engined tandem two-seater, which has been in use in successively refined versions since 1946. Its successor, the Yak-52 first appeared in 1977 and is very similar in layout to its predecessor. Both aircraft are fully aerobatic and single-seat versions have been produced for competition flying under the

ABOVE: The piston-engined Yak-18 has served in the training role since 1946, as well as competing in sundry aerobatic competitions. Since the late 1970s it has been gradually replaced by the Yak-52.

basic jet instruction was given on the Aero L-29 Delfin, with advanced training on the MiG-15UTI. The adoption of the Czechoslovakian L-29 and L-39 by the Soviet Air Force was an unusual departure from accepted practice, as virtually all other Warsaw Pact military aircraft are of Soviet design. However, the Polish Air Force uses the indigenous TS-11 Iskra for training, rather than the Czech-built L-29 and L-39 and Romania is currently acquiring the IAR 93 light attack aircraft designed and built in cooperation with Yugoslavia.

A small number of obsolescent MiG-17 single-seat fighters may remain in service for weapons and tactics training. In general, however, once a Soviet pilot has completed his advanced flying training he then begins his conversion training on an operational aircraft. With most multi-engined bomber and transport types, this can be accomplished by teaming the newly-qualified pilot as a co-pilot to a highly-qualified aircraft captain. Instruction on the single-seat fighter and attack aircraft is provided on modified two-seat conversion trainer variants. All of these are identified by the designation letter U (standing for *Uchebny* or training) and examples currently in use include the MiG-21U, MIG-23U, MiG-25U and Tu-22U. One squadron of each front-line fighter regiment is responsible for operational training and has a number of two-seat conversion trainers on strength in addition to its standard single-seat aircraft.

The maintenance of flying standards and adherence to flight safety regulations within the regiments is the responsibility of the units' commanding officers and qualified flying instructors. Each aircraft is fitted with a flight data recorder, which will reveal any examples of careless or unsafe flying. The regiment's commander is responsible for reviewing these recordings for each of his pilots and logging any incidents of poor airmanship. Corrective action can then be taken to ensure that mistakes are not repeated. However, in practice this system has been known to break down. The undisciplined and unsafe flying of one tactical fighter regiment based in Central Asia led to its officers being taken to task in the pages of the Soviet armed forces' newspaper *Red Star*. It is an interesting sidelight on Soviet military life that the publication attached the greater part of the blame for this incident not to the regiment's commander but to its Communist Party Organization.

auspices of DOSAAF. The same organization also operates the veteran An-2 Colt as a parachute training aircraft. Basic and advanced jet training is provided by the Aero L-39 Albatros, a tandem two-seat turbofan-powered trainer, which is designed and produced in Czechoslovakia. The L-39 has a maximum speed of 470mph and a range of 775 miles. It can carry a weapons load of 2400lb and is eminently suitable for basic training in tactics and weapons delivery. The Albatros therefore provides jet training from the basic stage up to the point when the pupil is ready to convert onto an operational aircraft. It is more economical to use a single jet trainer than two different types for basic and advanced jet training. Under the Soviet Air Force's earlier system

In spite of the much-publicized build-up of the Soviet Navy under Admiral Gorshkov during the 1970s, it is in naval air power alone that the United States can be said to have maintained a commanding lead over the Soviet Union. While the US Navy in the mid 1980s is building up to a strike carrier force of 15 major units, the Soviet Navy does not have a single fully-capable strike carrier in commission. A large, nuclear-powered attack aircraft carrier is under construction at Nikolayev. It has a displacement of 60,000 tons and can probably accommodate an air wing of 60 aircraft. Thus by the end of the present decade the first Soviet carrier capable of operating high performance jet strike fighters could be in commission. An air wing of 'navalized' MiG-23/27 Floggers or perhaps Su-27 Flankers would certainly represent a considerable advance in capabilities over the present-generation Yak-36 Forger VTOL naval fighters embarked aboard the *Kiev* class. One USAF intelligence officer has forecast that the Soviet Navy may have ten aircraft carriers in commission by the year 2000. This estimate must surely include VTOL carriers as well as true attack carriers and most probably reflects a 'worst case' assessment rather than a more realistic appraisal of the enormous effort required to introduce what is for the Soviet Navy an entirely new class of warship.

PREVIOUS PAGES: A US Navy SP-2H Neptune overflies the Soviet helicopter carrier *Moskva*.
BELOW: Soviet Navy pilots are pictured in front of a mixed array of Yak-36 fighters and Sukhoi Su-17s.

The Soviet Union's long neglect of the aircraft carrier is an indication firstly of that power's preoccupation with land warfare and secondly of the essentially defensive nature of its naval policy. Unlike the offensive US Navy policy, which regards its carrier battle groups as a means of power projection in support of worldwide interests, the decisions behind the Soviet naval build-up can be seen as a series of reactions to American initiatives. The initial impetus for the expansion of the Soviet Navy from a coastal defense force to an ocean-going fleet was the United States' acquisition of carrier-based nuclear bombers such as the AJ Savage and A3D Skywarrior in the 1950s. These weapons posed a direct threat to the Soviet homeland and needed to be countered as far from Soviet shores as possible by naval air, surface and submarine forces. In the 1960s the emphasis shifted to anti-submarine warfare (ASW) with the appearance of the Polaris SSBNs, although a residual threat remained from the carrier strike forces. In order to counter Polaris the Soviet Navy began to deploy into the eastern Mediterranean and Norwegian Sea. As the American SLBMs increased in range, firstly with improved versions of Polaris and later with Poseidon and Trident, so the Soviet Navy was forced to increase its area of operations. Trident missiles can reach targets in the Soviet Union when launched from

submarines lying in American home waters and so this necessitates a forward deployment of Soviet ASW systems. By the same token, Soviet Delta-class submarines can threaten the United States with SS-N-8 and SS-N-18 SLBMs from even greater ranges (as can the new Typhoon boats) and so a portion of the Soviet ASW effort must be reserved for guarding this valuable strategic asset against US Navy attack submarines.

TOP: Yakovlev's VTOL experiments in the mid 1960s with this aircraft, dubbed Freehand by NATO, bore fruit with the Yak-36 Forger.

ABOVE: Forgers on board *Novorossiisk*, third of the *Kiev*-class vessels to enter service. Some 40 Forgers are now operational with the Soviet Navy.

The priorities of Soviet naval strategy are most probably firstly the offensive against the American SSBN forces, secondly the safeguarding of its own strategic missile submarines and thirdly the elimination of the US Navy's aircraft carriers. The latter still carry nuclear-capable A-6 and A-7 attack aircraft, which although primarily tactical nuclear systems could threaten targets in the Soviet homeland. They will also be used to spearhead transoceanic reinforcement convoys to the aid of the NATO forces in Europe, or American allies in the Middle East and Pacific. The carriers' air wings can provide tactical air reinforcements to areas where Western air power is weak. Consequently the destruction of the US carriers will make a significant contribution to the support of Soviet land operations. Attacks on reinforcement convoys can be justified in the same way and are in accordance with the cherished Soviet military principle of action by all available forces being combined to achieve the main strategic objective. Independent naval missions have no such justification and are most probably regarded as military heresy by the Army-dominated Soviet General Staff. Therefore the Soviet carrier program is unlikely to be aimed at providing the Navy with an overseas power projection capability, although this could well be seen as a valuable bonus. It is more likely that the Soviet Union sees the aircraft carrier as an effective counter to SSBNs and vessels of its own kind. Interestingly enough, there does not seem to be agreement even within the Navy as to the value of the carrier in this role and some officers clearly think that the attack submarine is well able to deal with the threat.

At present the greater part of Soviet naval air power comprises land-based bombers and anti-submarine warfare aircraft. Total strength comprises some 775 combat aeroplanes and 300 combat helicopters, with 68,000 personnel. There are 360

ABOVE: A *Moskva*-class cruiser is circled by one of its Ka-25 Hormone ASW helicopters.

ABOVE LEFT AND LEFT: Kamov has long enjoyed a monopoly on the design and manufacture of Soviet shipboard helicopters. Like the pictured Ka-25s, all have contra-rotating main rotors.

RIGHT: An artist's impression of a *Kiev*-class cruiser/carrier in dry dock.

ABOVE: Operations on board *Kiev*, the first of a new class of 'mini aircraft carriers' to appear from 1976.

medium bombers in service for anti-shipping strike, 100 of them being modern Tu-26 Backfires. The 35 short-range Su-17s can either support naval infantry in amphibious operations, or carry out anti-shipping attacks in the Baltic Sea.

Long and medium-range electronic warfare and reconnaissance is undertaken by a force of 150 aircraft and 75 Tu-16s provide in-flight refueling. The land-based ASW patrol force of 190 aircraft includes 90 Be-12 Mail amphibians. Shipboard naval aircraft comprise 40 Yak-36 Forger VTOL fighters and over 150 Ka-25 Hormone and Ka-27 Helix helicopters. A further hundred or so Mi-14 Haze helicopters are used as shore-based ASW and mine-counter-

measures aircraft. The inventory of the Naval Air Force is completed by some 300 transport and training aircraft.

For the purposes of operational control the Naval Air Force (*Aviatsiya Voenno-Morskoyo Flota*) comes under the Navy Commander-in-Chief Admiral Gorshkov. It is commanded by Colonel-General of Aviation A A Mironenko, who has a staff comprising the Chief of Staff, Deputy Commander, Chief of the Political Department and Senior Aviation Engineer. The operational aircraft are divided amongst four fleet air forces: the Northern Fleet Air Force (405 aircraft), the Baltic Red Banner Fleet Air Force (275 aircraft), the Black Sea Fleet Air Force

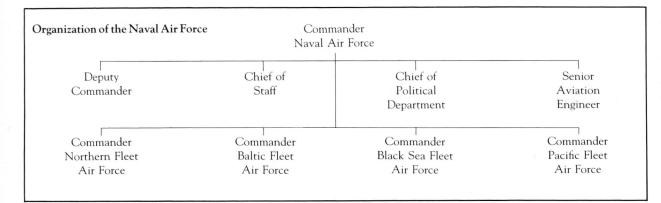

Organization of the Naval Air Force

		Commander Naval Air Force		
Deputy Commander	Chief of Staff		Chief of Political Department	Senior Aviation Engineer
Commander Northern Fleet Air Force	Commander Baltic Fleet Air Force		Commander Black Sea Fleet Air Force	Commander Pacific Fleet Air Force

BELOW: A *Moskva*-class helicopter carrier, with its internal hangar storage clearly visible towards the stern.
BOTTOM: *Kiev* combines the function of carrier and cruiser yet lacks the airborne early warning (AEW) or electronic warfare (EW) functions of true Western carriers, being designed primarily for sub-hunting.

(542 aircraft) and the Pacific Fleet Air Force (445 aircraft). As in Frontal Aviation, each Fleet Air Force is organized into divisions and regiments, except for the maritime reconnaissance, anti-submarine warfare and transport units which operate as independent regiments or squadrons. A Naval Air Force regiment is usually made up of two squadrons and there are two or three regiments in a division. The only major warships capable of operating aircraft in any numbers are the three *Kiev*-class VTOL carriers (usual complement 14 Yak-36 Forgers and 16 Ka-25 Hormones) and two *Moskva*-class ASW helicopter carriers (usual complement 18 Ka-25 Hormones). The fourth *Kiev*-class VTOL carrier, the *Kharkov*, joined the fleet in 1984. At present the two helicopter carriers and one *Kiev*-class VTOL carrier are serving with the Black Sea Fleet, which includes a Mediterranean squadron. The *Kiev*-class carriers *Minsk* and *Novorossiisk* are with the Pacific Fleet at Vladivostok, which detaches forces to the Indian Ocean.

BELOW: Action stations on board *Minsk*, second of the *Kiev*-class vessels to enter service. Hormone-A crews rush to their stations.

The primary role of the Soviet Navy and its Air Force is strategic anti-submarine warfare operations against the United States' SSBNs and those of Britain, France and the People's Republic of China. Since the 1960s, when the search for Polaris-SSBNs could be concentrated within the fairly confined limits of the Eastern Mediterranean and Norwegian Sea, this task has become progressively more difficult. Intercontinental-range SLBMs can be fired from sanctuary areas well-guarded by friendly air, surface and submarine defense forces. Alternatively they can be scattered to remote patrol areas where detection becomes even more problematical. It has been estimated that submarines armed with the Trident II SLBMs, which will enter US Navy service before the end of the 1980s, can operate within 53,000,000 square nautical miles of ocean and Moscow will at all times be within the range of their

missiles. This formidable capability will require Soviet ASW forces to extend their areas of operation to such distant seas as the South Pacific, if they are to cover the new submarines' entire patrol range. The future for Soviet strategic ASW operations against her main enemy is therefore, to say the least, uncertain. However, Soviet capabilities against the much smaller SSBN forces of the other nuclear powers may be more formidable, although Britain plans to have Trident II in service by the mid 1990s.

The problems of strategic ASW are by no means confined to the difficulty of finding sufficient forces to cover adequately large areas of ocean. Even if this is achieved, the capabilities of ASW equipment currently in service are by no means sufficient to guarantee a successful detection. For geographical reasons the Soviet Union is unable to use a system similar to the American SOSUS chains of fixed

ABOVE: A line-up of
Yak-36 Forger fighters
aboard *Minsk*.
RIGHT: A Forger on final
approach to *Kiev*, with
lift engines behind the
cockpit exposed. Unlike
the Harrier, separate
engines are utilized for
vertical lift and
forward flight.

long-range sonars, which act as a sort of underwater advanced warning system. Such sonar barriers must be positioned to cover oceanic choke points, for example the Greenland-Iceland-UK gap in the North Atlantic, and the Soviet Union does not of course control any sea areas through which even the older SSBNs must pass. Furthermore, the technically more-advanced United States' sonar systems depend to a large degree on the noisiness of Soviet submarines for their effectiveness. Soviet sonar equipment therefore suffers from the dual handicaps of a less efficient performance than that of its opponent's systems and the need for greater rather than the same efficiency in order to detect the quieter American SSBNs. These technical deficiencies apply equally to Soviet shipboard, aircraft and helicopter-mounted sonar equipment. Even though ASW is one area in which the Soviet Union is thought to have benefited from unauthorized tech-

nology transfers from the West, there can be no doubt of its relative backwardness in this area.

If geography and technology offer little help to the Soviet Navy in carrying out its primary mission, then aggressive tactical deployments may go a little way towards redressing the balance. The one certain factor amid the uncertainties of strategic ASW is that the SSBNs' patrols will start from their permanent shore bases. Therefore Soviet ASW forces have an opportunity of picking up the SSBNs at this point and thereafter trailing them. Attack submarines will be most useful for this purpose, but they are likely to be supported by *Kiev*-class carriers with their complement of Ka-25 Hormone ASW helicopters and Yak-36 Forgers to provide a limited degree of air cover. Shore-based patrol aircraft too can play their part. The Bear-F long-range ASW variant of the Tu-20, flying from bases in Cuba, has operated in the vicinity of the US Navy's SSBN

BELOW: A brace of Ka-27 Helix, a type now becoming operational in place of the smaller Hormone.
BOTTOM: The record-breaking Ka-32 was a forerunner of the Ka-27 which appeared in 1981.

Aircraft Strength of the Naval Air Force

Type	Role	No:
Tu-26 Backfire	MR bomber	100
Tu-22 Blinder	MR bomber	40
Tu-16 Badger	MR bomber	220
Su-17 Fitter	Attack	35
Yak-36 Forger	Shipboard fighter	40
Tu-20 Bear-F	LR ASW	50
Il-38 May	LR ASW	50
Be-12 Mail	ASW amphibian	90
Mi-14 Haze	ASW helicopter	90
Ka-25 Hormone	ASW helicopter	150
Ka-27 Helix	ASW helicopter	?
Tu-16 Badger	Recce/ECM	90
Tu-20 Bear	Recce	45
Tu-22 Blinder	Recce	5
An-12 Cub	ELINT	10
Il-18 Coot	ELINT	10
Tu-16 Badger	Tanker	75
Mi-14 Haze	MCM ⎫	
Mi-8 Hip	MCM ⎬	10

bases on the East Coast. However, the great problems with these tactics are that they require Soviet naval forces to penetrate heavily-defended sea areas. Therefore the chances of Soviet ASW forces successfully trailing all US Navy SSBNs on patrol and carrying out successful, coordinated attacks on them at the outbreak of war are remote.

The dubious effectiveness of Soviet ASW capabilities raises the entire question of the validity of Soviet naval doctrine. Is the ASW mission simply a cover for an expansion of general naval force? It is true that, as a land power, the Soviet Union would be unlikely to invest heavily in naval forces unless it saw this as a defense of its vital interests. The United States SSBN force certainly ranks as a serious threat to the Soviet homeland and has been used by Admiral Gorshkov as the justification for a significant naval build-up. The forces primarily intended to counter American SSBNs and aircraft carriers, such as attack submarines and long-range bombers, can perform a useful secondary mission against merchant shipping, for example. Naval warships can be used to 'show the flag' in Third World ports in peacetime and can spread Soviet influence through intervention in low-level conflicts. No doubt the Soviet naval leadership is well aware of these possibilities, but in order to maintain the forces needed to carry out these lesser missions it must do more than just pay lip service to the primacy of the strategic ASW mission. It must rather tailor its entire fleet structure around the requirements of that operational role.

There is much evidence that it has done exactly that. The effort expended on aircraft-carrying ships has produced warships with a large complement of ASW helicopters in the *Kiev* and *Moskva* classes. A small number of the Ka-25 Hormones embarked on these vessels are equipped with search radars for reconnaissance and over-the-horizon missile targeting and the *Kiev* class carries the Yak-36 Forger for air defense and also for anti-shipping strikes and ground attack. Yet these capabilities are quite clearly secondary to the ASW role for which the air components of both the helicopter and VTOL carriers are best suited. There is little reason to doubt Admiral Gorshkov's assertion that the *Kiev* class are 'the most powerful forces intended for search and destruction of enemy nuclear-powered submarines in distant ocean areas.'

The Ka-25 Hormone is not only carried by the *Kiev* and *Moskva* classes, but also by warships such as the battlecruiser *Kirov*; *Kara*, *Kresta* I and II and *Kynda* class cruisers; and *Sovremennyy*, *Udaloy*, *Kashin*, *Kanin* and *Kotlin* class destroyers. The Ka-25 is a notably compact design with an overall length of 34ft and maximum weight of 15,500lb. It is powered by two 900shp Glushenkov GTD-3 turboshafts driving 51ft 8in diameter coaxial rotors. Performance is relatively modest, with a maximum speed of 135mph and a range of 400 miles when external fuel tanks are carried. The Hormone-A ASW variant carries two pilots and two or three systems operators in its capacious cabin. Its operational equipment includes a search radar mounted beneath the nose, a towed magnetic anomaly detector, possibly ESM (electronic support measures) sensors to detect radio and radar emission and, most importantly, sonobuoys and a dunking sonar. A ventral weapons bay can carry two acoustic-homing torpedoes or depth charges. Ka-25s may operate in hunter/killer pairs, with one helicopter operating its dunking sonar while the other positions itself for the kill. Alternatively, in the case of the smaller warships which only carry one helicopter, it could cooperate with its parent ship in submarine hunting, or even operate independently. A number of Soviet ASW ships,

OPPOSITE: A Ka-27 Helix lands on the guided missile carrier *Udaloy* during exercises in 1981.
OPPOSITE BELOW: *Minsk*, the largest of the three vessels in convoy, takes on fuel in the Western Pacific. Her escort, the guided missile cruiser *Kara*, does likewise.

BELOW: The *Moskva* is pictured with its complement of Ka-25 ASW helicopters.

RIGHT: A Ka-25 Hormone flies in the sunset. The type replaced the Mi-4 on board Soviet vessels in the 1960s, since which time it has served with admirable reliability.

LEFT: Close-up of Mil's Mi-14 Haze, a belated ASW variant of the Mi-8 which first appeared in 1976. Features include a seaworthy hull and large search radar in an under-nose bulge.

including the *Moskva* and *Kiev* classes, carry the 18-mile-range SS-N-14 anti-submarine missile, which could make use of target data transmitted from a Ka-25 to the parent ship.

The Hormone-B version of the Ka-25 is fitted with a powerful surface-search radar and is used to provide mid-course guidance for long-range anti-shipping missiles. The elderly SS-N-3 with a range of 280 miles and the later SS-N-12 with a 620 mile range require a target detection capability of longer range than the parent ship's radar if they are to be used to full effect. A Ka-25 operating up to its ceiling of 16,500ft can greatly extend the radar search coverage. Once a target has been acquired, it will transmit the necessary data back to the warship. The missile is then launched and any necessary corrections can be commanded by the ship so long as the missile remains within line of sight; however once it falls beneath the radar horizon this function must be taken over by the helicopter. Two of the *Kiev* class's complement of Ka-25s are generally Hormone-B versions. A third version of the Ka-25, identified as Hormone-C, is used for utility transport and search and rescue duties aboard the VTOL carriers.

With more than 150 examples in service with the Naval Air Force, the Ka-25 Hormone serves in greater numbers than any other naval aircraft and it probably ranks second in importance only to the attack submarine as a forward-based strategic ASW system. Yet it is an old design which first appeared in 1961 and is likely to be replaced by the superficially very similar Ka-27 Helix during the next few years. The Helix (which some sources designate as the Ka-32) first appeared aboard the helicopter platform of the destroyer *Udaloy* in the Baltic during 1981. Its dimensions are similar to those of the earlier helicopter, with a length of 36ft 1in and a rotor diameter of 52ft 2in, and therefore it will be able to operate from all ships which can accommodate the Ka-25. However, the Ka-27 is a much heavier aircraft, with a maximum weight of some 23,000lb, and is likely to have more powerful engines, a greater range and better ASW sensors and weapons than its predecessor. Two versions have been identified: the Helix-A with search radar, dipping sonar, sonobuoys and towed magnetic anomaly detector for ASW, and the

Helix-B for over-the-horizon, surface-to-surface missile guidance. It is possible that the Helix-B will be given a secondary role as an ECM jamming platform to defend the parent ship against missiles.

The operational role of the Yak-36 Forger single-seat VTOL aircraft embarked aboard the *Kiev*-class carriers is by no means immediately apparent. However, what is clear is that it is in no sense a Soviet equivalent of the British V/STOL Sea Harrier, as it lacks both that fighter's air-to-air combat agility and its weapons capacity in air-to-surface roles. Logically, the Yak-36's primary role would be air defense of its carrier and accompanying escorts, with anti-shipping attack and ship-to-shore air strike as secondary missions. However, if this were the case, it is surprising that the Forger has not been fitted with a search radar (it does have a small ranging radar) and a built-in gun armament for the air-to-air role. Forgers have been photographed carrying gun

pods and AA-8 Aphid IR-homing AAMs and also the AS-7 Kerry ASM, which is used by Frontal Aviation's ground-attack fighters.

The distinction between a VTOL (vertical take-off and landing) and V/STOL (vertical/short take-off and landing) aircraft is an important one. The VTOL Forger is a far less capable aircraft than the V/STOL Harrier, most notably because it must take-off vertically and so cannot increase its payload by using rolling take-off and ski-jump ramp techniques. Nor can the VTOL Forger use the 'viffing' (vectoring in forward flight) maneuvers which make the Sea Harrier such a formidable opponent in a dog-fight. Unlike the Harrier which uses a single power-plant for both vertical and forward flight, the Yak-36 has a lift-cruise engine (delivering some 16,500lb thrust) and two 5500lb lift jets. The latter are shut down during forward flight, when they become so much dead weight, and should either of

BELOW: The twin-turboprop Beriev Be-12 Mail has rendered sterling service as a coastal patrol craft since its introduction in the early 1960s. It has also set many world records.

them fail to restart when the Forger wishes to transition from forward to vertical flight then the aircraft must be abandoned as it cannot make an emergency landing on only one. However, on the credit side the Yak-36's transition from vertical to horizontal flight at take-off and vice versa on landing has been observed to be very smooth and stable – although it is a comparatively protracted process.

The Forger then – warts and all – is likely to undertake the Soviet Navy's shipboard fighter mission throughout the 1980s. Its performance at altitude is supersonic (Mach 1.2 at 36,000ft), but at low level maximum speed drops to around 650mph or Mach 0.85. Service ceiling is 46,000ft and combat radius 150 miles. This is not a scintillating performance by the standards of shore-based interceptors (and comes nowhere near the phenomenal capabilities of the US Navy's F-14 Tomcat shipboard defense fighters). Yet, as Britain's experience in the South Atlantic conflict of 1982 demonstrated, theoretical combat capabilities are not necessarily an infallible guide to actual performance on operations. If Royal Navy Sea Harriers with their Mach 0.95 maximum speed could defend a naval task force against Mach 2 Mirage IIIs, then there are probably certain conditions under which the Yak-36 will perform effectively. It will certainly pose a serious threat to long-range maritime patrol aircraft such as the US Navy's P-3 Orion.

The Naval Air Force's long-range ASW capability is augmented by shore-based Tu-20 Bear-F and Il-38 May patrol aircraft, with fifty of each currently in service. The Bear-F is one of the most recent variants of the 1950s-vintage Tu-20 intercontinental-range strategic bomber to appear and surprisingly it remains in production. The design's greatest advantage for the strategic ASW mission is its unrefueled combat radius of more than 5000 miles. Bear-Fs can operate from Soviet overseas bases in Angola, Ethiopia, South Yemen, Cuba and Vietnam, which greatly extends the area of ocean that they can cover. The use of Cuba as an advanced base is especially valuable, as it allows the approaches to the US Navy's East Coast submarine bases to be monitored. ASW equipment carried by the Bear-F is likely to include a search radar, sonobuoys and related acoustic processing equipment and a magnetic anomaly detector.

The Il-38 May is a conversion of the Il-18 airliner design for the ASW patrol mission. It is powered by four 5200shp Ivchenko AI-20M turboprops, which give it a maximum speed of 400mph and cruising speed of 290mph. Endurance is 16 hours and maximum range 5200 miles. Unlike the Tu-20, which carries a nose mounted in-flight refueling probe, the Il-38 cannot be refueled in flight and so in terms of operating range it is a less useful design. However, as it started life as an airliner, it has ample space in a large internal cabin to house electronic equipment, ASW sensor operators' stations and rest accommodation for relief crewmembers. In this respect it is far better suited to the ASW mission than the Bear-F, with its relatively restricted fuselage accommodation. The Il-38 first appeared in the early 1970s, probably in response to the US Navy's introduction of the 2500-mile range Poseidon SLBM. The farther-ranging Bear-F is most probably an early countermeasure to the 4600-mile-range Trident I.

The ASW sensors carried by the Il-38 include a search radar mounted beneath the forward fuselage. This will be useful in detecting the snort tube of the diesel-electric submarine or the periscope of a nuclear-powered attack boat. It is also of course valuable against surface targets, as the Il-38 can combine a secondary maritime reconnaissance mission with its ASW role. At the rear of the fuselage a tail boom extension carries a magnetic anomaly detector. This is a short-range sensor used to confirm a submarine's position during an attack run. It is mounted as far away from sources of magnetic interference within the aircraft as possible. The most useful sensors for submarine detection, however, are air-dropped sonobuoys. These are in effect miniature sonars which can be sown in patterns and transmit bearings on any underwater object back to the ASW aircraft. There are two types: passive sonobuoys,

BELOW: Ilyushin's conversion of the Il-18 airliner to produce the Il-38 May ASW aircraft parallels the development of the US P-3 Orion from the civilian Electra airliner. The May first appeared in the early 1970s.

which listen out for underwater sounds and are used for long-range search, and active sonobuoys which transmit a sound wave that is reflected back from the target and are used during the latter stages of a submarine hunt to obtain more precise bearings on the target. Acoustic processing equipment aboard the ASW aircraft will interpret the raw data obtained by the sonobuoys. For example, it will distinguish between the sounds made by marine life and those of a submarine. It will even be able to identify the nationality and class of boat from its 'sound signature.' The effectiveness of all this advanced electronic equipment will determine the operational usefulness of the aircraft which carries it. Soviet ASW sensors do not perform as well as their western counterparts and even with the latest technology ASW operations are at best a hit-or-miss affair. Consequently the US Navy is confident of the near-invulnerability of its SSBNs. However, should one be detected, the Il-38 is well armed to deal with it, carrying acoustic-homing torpedoes, conventional and nuclear depth charges in its weapons bay.

Short range ASW operations are primarily concerned with the protection of SSBN bases and the submarines' sanctuary areas in home waters. The Soviet Navy's SSBNs are concentrated in the Northern Fleet, based on the Kola Peninsula in the White Sea, and the Pacific Fleet with its headquarters at Vladivostok on the Sea of Japan. Therefore to counter enemy attack submarines short-range ASW forces will be deployed in these sea areas. These include the Naval Air Force's 90 Mi-14 Haze shore-based ASW helicopters and the same number of Be-12 Mail amphibians. They will also undertake a general coastal defense role along the Soviet Union's Pacific, Black Sea, Baltic and Arctic coastlines. The Arctic Ocean in particular has a special strategic significance for the Soviet Union and it has been reported that one of the Soviet SSBNs' patrol areas is beneath the polar icecap.

The Be-12 is particularly suited to the coastal patrol task and it is probably no coincidence that the only other major air arm to fly ASW amphibians (the Japanese naval air arm) also operates in the north west Pacific. The Be-12 is a twin-turboprop, with a high-mounted gull wing which has given it the nickname *Tchaika* (Seagull). Power is provided by 4190shp Ivchenko AI-20D turboprops, giving a maximum speed of 380mph and a range of 2500 miles. Its maximum take-off weight is 66,000lb and the Be-12's considerable payload-lifting capabilities have been demonstrated by the gaining of several world records for flying boats. The main-wheel members of the *Tchaika*'s tailwheel undercarriage retract into the side of the flying-boat hull. This amphibious capability gives the aircraft a useful secondary air-sea rescue role. Its ASW equipment includes a search radar mounted in the nose above a glazed navigator's position and a tail-mounted magnetic anomaly detector. Depth charges can be mounted on underwing pylons and sonobuoys are probably carried within the hull.

The Mi-14 Haze ASW helicopter is an adaptation of the Mi-8 Hip, fitted with a retractable undercarriage and a watertight hull and side-mounted sponsons to give it an amphibious capability. Much of the Mi-14's airframe is similar to that of the assault transport helicopter, but its powerplant is almost certainly the improved Isotov TV-3 turboshaft. This would give the Haze a maximum speed of about 155 mph. ASW equipment carried by the Haze-A includes a nose-mounted

search radar, a towed magnetic anomaly detector and dunking sonar. Offensive armament could be either depth charges or acoustic homing torpedoes. The Mi-14 operates exclusively from shore bases as it is too large an aircraft to use the helicopter platforms of the smaller warships or fit on the elevators of the *Kiev*-class carriers.

The Haze-B is a mine countermeasures adaptation of the ASW helicopter. A small number of Mi-14s together with a few Mi-8s (totalling about 20 helicopters) are probably responsible for keeping the main SSBN bases and their approaches clear of mines. They are likely to operate in cooperation with coastal minesweepers but because they can only tow a sweep in low sea states, their work will concentrate on clearing harbors and sheltered waters. If Soviet helicopter minesweeping techniques are similar to those of the US Navy, in addition to operating a towed sweep the MCM Mi-14s and Mi-8s will also tow acoustic and magnetic sweeping devices. As well as its defensive mine warfare capabilities, the Soviet Union, with the largest stocks of sea mines of any world power, is well-equipped for offensive operations and the long-range aircraft of the Naval Air Force will undertake this role.

The third major mission of the Soviet Navy, after offensive ASW and protection of friendly SSBNs, is the elimination of the US Navy's attack carriers. This will be attempted by surface, submarine and air attack, with the Naval Air Force's bombers taking a leading part. The Tu-26 Backfire is by far the most capable naval bomber with 100 currently in naval service. As deliveries of the Backfire have been equally divided between the Aviation Armies of the Soviet Union and the Naval Air Force, the anti-carrier mission is clearly an important one. Moreover, as the AASU may well be called upon to reinforce the Naval Air Force's anti-carrier bomber forces, the mission must rank equal in importance to theater strategic bombing operations in Soviet eyes. The assumption that the Soviet Navy regards air attack as one of the best ways of dealing with the American carriers is implicit in this argument. The large force of nuclear-powered attack submarines will be primarily concerned with the strategic ASW mission. Therefore the Tu-26 is likely to spearhead the attack on the carrier battle groups, backed up by submarine attack and surface and submarine-launched long-range anti-shipping missiles.

A coordinated attack by air, surface and submarine forces is likely, because the Soviet Navy is well aware of the considerable defensive strength of the carrier battle group and must realize that its best chance of success is in swamping these defenses with

ABOVE: The addition of the potent Tu-26 Backfire to Soviet Naval Aviation (some 100 currently serving) has put the US Navy's carrier force under a new threat. This example carries the AS-4 Kitchen stand-off missile, but the AS-6 can also be carried.

ABOVE: A Yak-36 Forger lands on *Kiev*.
BELOW: The Mi-14 Haze land-based ASW helicopter trails a Magnetic Anomaly Detection 'bird.'
OPPOSITE: A fine study of the Ka-25 Hormone. This example is landing on the helicopter platform of a *Kresta* II-class cruiser.

a multiplicity of threats. Air attacks will be made by waves of bombers, approaching from several directions to launch stand-off missile attacks, possibly followed up by low-level bombing. The Tu-26 Backfire's stand-off missile armament at present comprises the AS-4 Kitchen and possibly also the AS-6 Kingfish. The former has a maximum range of 180 miles and a speed of Mach 2, whereas the AS-6's range is 135 miles but it is faster at Mach 3. The AS-6 makes use of radar terminal homing; either by switching on an active radar which will pick up the carrier's large radar 'signature', or using a passive seeker to guide onto the ship's own radar emissions.

Both the AS-4 and AS-6 can be fitted with either a high explosive or a nuclear warhead. A Mach 3.5 ASM with a range of 500 miles is being developed as a replacement for the Kingfish. Backfire-equipped Naval bomber regiments serve with both the Northern and Pacific Fleet Air Forces. They have a sufficiently good unrefueled range to cover most of the North Atlantic and the greater part of the Western Pacific, although they would need to refuel in flight (or to stage through the former American naval airfield at Cam Ranh Bay in Vietnam) to reach the important chokepoint at the Malacca Strait.

The large force of 220 naval Tu-16 Badger-C and G bombers will be considerably less effective against the carrier battle groups than the Backfires, as in contrast to the Tu-26's Mach 2 performance the elderly Tu-16's maximum speed is only Mach 0.9. However, they will be useful in making follow-up attacks in the wake of the more capable Backfires and can be used against less well defended naval forces and merchant shipping. The Badger-G is armed with the AS-6 or the earlier AS-5 Kelt ASMs, the latter having a range of nearly 200 miles at a speed of Mach 0.9. The naval bomber force also includes 40 Tu-22 Blinders, which can attack with free-fall bombs. These naval bomber forces, perhaps augmented by aircraft from the AASU, can certainly mount a formidably strong and carefully orchestrated attack on the Navy's precious aircraft carriers. However, they will have to run the gauntlet of a well conceived, layered defense system with its outer edge several hundred miles from the carrier itself.

Various naval aircraft will play important supporting roles in the air-sea battle, including air reconnaissance, electronic intelligence-gathering, electronic warfare and in-flight refueling. The first priority will be to locate enemy naval forces and this will be undertaken by Tu-16 Badger-D, Tu-22 Blinder-C and Tu-20 Bear-D aircraft, together with

specially-launched radar-reconnaissance satellites. The Bear-D, which carries a large search radar in a ventral radome, is also able to provide over-the-horizon targeting for ship and submarine-launched SS-N-3 Shaddock and SS-N-12 Sandbox anti-ship missiles. Electronic intelligence is also a valuable mission, both for its immediate usefulness in locating enemy forces and for the information of longer term value it provides on their electronic systems. The Naval Air Force operates a wide range of ELINT aircraft, including Tu-16 Badger-E, F and K variants, An-12 Cub-Bs and Il-18 Coot-As. The more active electronic warfare mission of ECM jamming and 'spoofing' is undertaken by Badger-H and J. This will be of particular value to bombers attempting to penetrate the carrier battle groups' early warning radar screens. Yet perhaps the most significant of all the support missions is that of in-flight refueling, as the Naval Air Force's 75 Tu-16 Badger tanker aircraft enable the range and endurance of its operational aircraft to be increased.

Unlike the United States the Soviet Union does not have a substantial amphibious warfare capability and there is certainly no Soviet equivalent of the US Marine Corps aviation units. However, there is a force of Soviet Naval Infantry, 14,500 men strong, which is attached to each of the Soviet fleets. Their role is likely to be short-range, seaward-flanking assaults in cooperation with a full-scale land offensive. Just as the airborne forces could be used against enemy airfields, the Naval Infantry could be used to seize and hold important ports. Amphibious assaults would be especially valuable in support of a Soviet attempt to break out from the Baltic or Black Seas. Air support for such operations would be provided by Frontal Aviation. However, each Naval Infantry force does have a number of Mi-8 Hip-E armed

assault-transport helicopters on strength, although these cannot of course be operated from warships. There are also a number of fixed-wing and helicopter transports attached to each fleet for airlift support and these could be used by the Naval Infantry. The Naval Air Force's 35 Su-17 fighter-bombers could also provide them with air support. Naval Infantry assaults are made by landing craft or hovercraft, although the Soviet Navy's only amphibious landing ship, the *Ivan Rogov*, can operate up to four Ka-25 Hormones. A limited Soviet overseas intervention capability could be built around ships of this type, perhaps carrying Ka-27 Helix helicopters. Limited air support could be provided by the Forgers of *Kiev*-class ships. However, this would be a very makeshift arrangement. It shows how far the Soviet Union is from acquiring an amphibious warfare capability comparable to the United States'.

The build-up of Soviet naval aviation over the past two decades has been characterized by a steady improvement in capabilities and a widening of areas of operation. There have been no far-reaching changes in operational doctrine, such as those brought about by the Air Force's acquisition of the Su-24 Fencer and MiG-27 Flogger. Even the change from a nuclear to a conventional warfighting doctrine in the 1970s did not lead to any great changes in tactics, organization, or equipment. The appearance of the *Kiev* and her Yak-36 Forgers was certainly not the dawn of a new era for the Naval Air Force. Yet the acquisition of the highly-capable Tu-26 Backfire and the increasing use of overseas air bases has certainly increased the power and reach of Soviet naval aviation. Whether the 1990s will bring about a revolution in Soviet naval air doctrine, with the first carrier battle groups to sail under the hammer and sickle, remains to be seen.

OPPOSITE AND BELOW: Hovercraft play an important role in Soviet amphibious assaults, carrying both armored vehicles and personnel. Three classes, Gus, Lebed and Aist, are in service: the last-named is pictured here.

CHAPTER NINE

SOVIET AIR POWER IN ACTION

PREVIOUS PAGES: An Su-22, the export version of Sukhoi's ground-attack Su-17, in Libyan Air Force service. BELOW: A rather earlier ground attack stalwart in Soviet service was the Ilyushin Il-2 Shturmovik of World War II vintage. OPPOSITE: Gary Powers (INSET), whose U-2 spyplane was downed by a Soviet SAM in 1960 and (MAIN PICTURE) one of the reconnaissance photographs he took.

During the four decades since the end of the Great Patriotic War of 1945 Soviet air power has undergone many radical changes. Yet it is first and foremost to this epic struggle that the Soviet air leaders look not only for inspiration and a source of tradition but also for concrete lessons in air warfare. At first sight at any rate, change rather than continuity would seem to be the *leitmotiv* in the postwar history of the Soviet air forces. The massed Soviet air armies of 1944-45 flew piston-engined bombers, attack aircraft and fighters – the great majority of its aircraft being single-engined fighters of largely wooden construction, rather than the metal airframes then invariably used for combat aircraft by the other major combatant nations. Soviet aircraft lacked such advanced equipment as airborne radar, by 1945 in widespread use elsewhere, or guided missiles which the Luftwaffe had used in action. The most serious of the Soviet Air Force's deficiencies, however, was its backwardness in developing turbojet engines. By the end of World War II only the Soviet Union among the major world powers had failed to build and fly a jet-powered aircraft. During the first postwar decade many of these technical shortcomings were made good, often with the help of captured German technology.

The far-reaching changes in combat aircraft design brought about by the introduction of jet engines, together with the revolution in warfare ushered in by the invention of nuclear weapons, combined to transform the nature of war in the air. The Soviet armed forces were notably reluctant to come to terms with the new conditions of warfare. The strength of the postwar Soviet Army was fixed

at over 3,000,000 men and was only reduced (by a massive 1,800,000 men) in the mid 1950s and similarly the Air Force, which ended the war with a strength of about 17,000 aircraft, had increased in strength to 20,000 aircraft by the early 1950s. Yet during the course of the 1950s the Soviet forces did make the transition from a conventional to a nuclear warfighting strategy. The Soviet atom bomb was first tested in 1949 and a thermonuclear weapon was successfully detonated four years later. The Air Force's hitherto-neglected *Dal'nyaya aviatsiya* (Long Range Aviation) was expanded and reequipped with medium-range Tu-16 and long-range Tu-20 and Mya-4 jet bombers to carry out the nuclear delivery mission.

Concern over the strength of the USAF's nuclear striking force, with Strategic Air Command's bombers deployed to forward bases in Europe, North Africa and the Far East led to a parallel expansion of air defense forces, which became an independent service in 1954. At the end of the Great Patriotic War there had been no nationwide Soviet air defense system and so a network of ground radars, AA artillery, interceptors and surface-to-air missiles was hastily put together in order to close massive gaps in strategic air defense coverage. By 1960 the process was nearing completion and in May that year one of the United States Central Intelligence Agency's high flying U-2 reconnaissance aircraft was brought down by a SAM over Sverdlovsk. Since 1956 such reconnaissance flights had been mounted over the entire Soviet Union virtually on a routine basis. Another sign of Soviet progress in developing modern weaponry was the launch of Sputnik I, the

ABOVE: A MiG-23 in Libyan colors. The Libyans were given a number of MiG-23U trainers in addition to the pictured single-seat fighter version.

BELOW: Mikoyan's formidably fast Foxbat interceptor fighter, with four AA-6 missiles underwing.

ABOVE: A Soviet
Foxbat-E in 'clean'
configuration selects
reheat for a swift escape
from its photographer.

first artificial satellite to be boosted into earth orbit, in 1957. Shortly afterwards the SS-6 Sapwood ICBM became operational and this milestone in the growth of Soviet military power was marked by the elevation of the Strategic Rocket Forces to the status of an independent service in May 1960.

The rise in importance of the strategic offensive and defensive aircraft and missile forces was accompanied by a decline in the strength and prestige of Frontal Aviation. The command's 20,000 aircraft of the early 1950s was an artificially inflated strength, resulting from the retention of older piston-engined types at the same time that the new generation of jet warplanes was coming into service. Frontal Aviation's strength quickly fell to around 12,000 aircraft, as the piston-engined types were retired. The

Shturmovik or specialized ground-attack aircraft completely disappeared from the Soviet Air Force when the Il-10 was phased out at this time. Tactical air power in the 1950s was primarily provided by MiG-15 and later MiG-17 and MiG-19 jet fighters, which had a secondary ground-attack role, and the Il-28 light bomber.

As the Soviet air forces entered the 1960s it seemed that they had irrevocably abandoned the strategic, operational and tactical lessons of the Great Patriotic War as irrelevant to a nuclear conflict. The new decade was largely a period of consolidation, as the strategic forces were progressively reinforced and modernized. However, one new trend to emerge was the Soviet emphasis on land-based strategic missile forces, for whereas the United States pursued a parallel development of bombers and ICBMs for the strategic mission, the Soviet Union concentrated on the development and production of missiles. Tactical air power too continued along the course already set during the 1950s, with more modern MiG-21 fighters and Yak-28 light bombers replacing the earlier types. By the end of the decade its front-line strength has fallen to around 5000 aircraft. Yet even the modernized Soviet air forces of the 1960s retained some of its links with the past. All of the senior commanders were veterans of the Great Patriotic War, of course, and the organization of tactical air power into air armies, divisions and regiments was virtually unchanged from the wartime pattern.

The Soviet rediscovery of the utility of conventional warfare in the 1970s was a result of its achievement of strategic nuclear parity with the United States – a situation which was formally recognized by the negotiation of the SALT I agreement in 1972. If the Soviet Union possessed roughly equivalent (or preferably superior) nuclear forces to the United States at both strategic and theater levels, then the latter would be restrained from using them to counter an attack by conventional forces. This situation opened up new possibilities for the offensive use of tactical air and land forces in swift and hard-hitting operations which could achieve decisive results before the enemy would be able to concentrate his defenses. Consequently Soviet military doctrine today, while still recognizing the

RIGHT: Mikoyan's first production jet, the MiG-15, saw early action in Korea and, later in the 1950s, the Middle East. An Egyptian example is pictured here.

BELOW: Although of mid-1950s origin, the MiG-21 still serves widely with Soviet and Warsaw Pact air forces. A Yugoslav Air Force example is pictured.

possibility of nuclear war and preparing for it, also envisages the possibility of large-scale conventional conflict. This shift in operational doctrine during the 1970s coincided with a flood of Soviet literature on the battles of the Great Patriotic War. Therefore, just as military experts have identified the inspiration for the Soviet Army's present Operational Maneuver Group strategy in the history of the campaigns of 1944-45, so a number of recent trends in air force operational doctrine originate in the experience of 1941-45.

The Soviet Air Force's former commander-in-chief, Marshal Kutakhov, testified to the importance of the lessons of the Great Patriotic War in finding solutions to present-day operational problems. He also identified in his own writings a number of significant historical examples which have a bearing on modern air doctrine. For example, he was critical of the Soviet Air Force's failure to attack German rear areas during the Smolensk, Kharkov and Orel offensive of 1943. The major innovation of modern Soviet tactical air power of course is its capability to attack enemy forces throughout the depth of their deployment. Kutakhov also criticized the poor coordination of the air armies during 1943. This too has a bearing on present day concerns, as one of the main reasons for the major reorganization of Soviet tactical air power in the early 1980s was the need to improve the coordination of these forces in combat. The two examples cited are all the more noteworthy because in general Soviet historical writings are reluctant to criticize the performance of the armed forces. There are some striking similarities between the World War II experience and recent developments in Soviet air power. The operational employment of the Mi-24 Hind in close support of ground forces is a return to the close-knit operations of tank forces and *Shturmovik* regiments. The high performance of jet aircraft makes such cooperation very difficult be-

tween modern fighter-bombers and armies, but the relatively slow speed and low operating altitude of helicopters is well suited to the traditional close air support mission.

The reorganization of the Air Defense Forces represents an interesting compromise between historical experience and the requirements of modern technology. By subordinating the air defense command to that of the theater of military operations, the Soviet High Command has restored the close relationship between the army commander and his air cover which existed during the Great Patriotic War. Yet at the same time, the air defense forces in the field have been integrated within the entire national air defense organization so that they can contribute to strategic air defense. Wartime experience has often resulted in a distinctive Soviet view of air operations, which is quite different from Western conceptions. For example, in Soviet eyes air superiority is the ability to concentrate overwhelming air strength at the decisive point of the combat theater, rather than an attempt to gain ascendancy over the entire area of operations. Above all, the Great Patriotic War has shown the Soviet forces the need for constant military preparedness, as the Soviet Union was brought very near to defeat in the battles of 1941-42. In a future war they will not be caught unprepared, nor will the Soviet homeland again be the battleground.

The Soviet armed forces' preoccupation with the lessons of the Great Patriotic War only serves to highlight the fact that they have seen very little combat service since that time. There was no direct clash between the Soviet Air Force and the USAF over Korea in 1950-53, although Soviet-manufactured fighters were certainly engaged and Soviet advisors and combat instructors most probably flew with their Chinese pupils in combat. The results of the air battles between MiG-15s and USAF F-86 Sabres over the Yalu River can have given the

Soviet air commanders no reason for complacency.

At the final reckoning the US Air Force had destroyed 792 MiGs for the loss of only 78 Sabres. This ten-to-one victory ratio was achieved despite the fact that the MiG-15 outperformed the Sabre in several important respects. Most notably it had a greater operational ceiling, giving it the initial advantage of superior height and allowing the MiG-15 pilot to choose the time and place of combat. The MiG-15 could outclimb the Sabre at all altitudes and its initial acceleration in a dive was better, although the heavier American fighter had the advantage in a sustained dive and was marginally faster in level flight. However, these good points were offset by such disadvantages as poor control at high speed, a low rate of roll and instability at high altitudes. Yet, while acknowledging that the Sabre was probably the better aircraft overall, the Chinese MiG-15 pilots had two important tactical advantages. They invariably operated in greater numbers than their American opponents and the combats took place within a few minutes' flying time of their bases, whereas the Sabres were near the limits of their range. On balance the deciding factor was the superior tactical skill, experience and personal qualities of the American fighter pilots. Whether the results would have been different if Soviet pilots had been fully committed to Korea can only be conjectured. It is difficult to form any firm conclusions about the standards of the Soviet Air Force of the 1950s from the Korean War experience, as in Soviet hands the MiG-15s might have been flown more effectively.

The same caution should be applied to an assessment of the Soviet Air Defense Forces based on the performance of the North Vietnamese air defenses in 1965-72, which made use of Soviet-supplied equipment and tactics. However, as much of weaponry was less modern than that in Soviet service, the experience of the Vietnam War is really only relevant to an assessment of individual weapons and not to the overall performance of the integrated Soviet air defense system. Therefore, the shortcomings of the SA-2 Guideline surface-to-air missile, which is still in widespread service with the Air Defense Forces, cannot necessarily be taken to reflect deficiencies in the Soviet air defenses as a

BELOW: The SA-2 Guideline served alone in Vietnam, where its deficiencies were cruelly exposed. Yet it is only one of a series of complementary missile systems, and as such is still in use today.

whole. In Vietnam it was the only SAM system available, whereas it is only one of a series of complementary missile systems in Soviet service. In 1967 the North Vietnamese fired 55 SA-2s for every aircraft brought down, while by 1972 when American countermeasures had considerably improved it required 150 missiles to achieve the same result. Yet these statistics do not tell the complete story, as in order to avoid the height bands (20,000ft to 40,000ft) where aircraft were most vulnerable to SAMs, the American strike aircraft were forced to operate at heights between 12,000ft and 15,000ft. Not only was their fuel consumption greater at these heights, and their operational flexibility consequently reduced, but their vulnerability to AA artillery fire was greater. Thus in evading the SA-2's most effective altitudes, the American aircraft were exposed to another threat and in fact 68 percent of aircraft losses were due to this cause.

The North Vietnamese air defenses comprised SA-2 missiles, a wide range of AA artillery (mostly 37mm, 57mm, 85mm and 100mm) and MiG-17, MiG-19 and MiG-21 interceptors. All were linked by a command and control system and supported by some 200 early-warning, GCI (ground control interception) and fire-control radars. The interceptors operated under strict control from the ground, following the classic Soviet interception tactics which have only very recently been relaxed to allow pilots more initiative. The controllers would not only direct fighters into a position for an interception, but would themselves make the decision as to whether to launch the attack or break off the engagement. The North Vietnamese fighter force was never a large one, numbering 66 aircraft in 1966 and 145 by 1972. Nor was its performance in

ABOVE: US personnel inspect a captured Syrian MiG-19. Though the type has long since passed from front-line Soviet use, it formed the (unlicensed) basis of the Chinese F-6 and F-9 series of fighters.

LEFT: The SA-2 Guideline SAM saw extensive use in the Six Day War of 1967, where it was supplemented by the low-altitude SA-3 and operated for Egypt under Soviet control.

UNCRATED FUSELAGE AND TAIL SECTION

BEAGLES BEING ASSEMBLED

combat outstanding, when judged by the yardstick of victories and losses. The Americans lost 92 aircraft in air combat and in return destroyed 193 North Vietnamese fighters. Yet it represented a further serious problem for American strike aircraft, which were already under threat of attack from SAMs and AA artillery. In short the effectiveness of the defense lay not so much in the individual performance of its component parts as in the cumulative results achieved by a multiplicity of threats.

In 1968 the Soviet Air Force itself went into action in Europe – not against the NATO Alliance but rather against Czechoslovakia, a Warsaw Pact ally. The ending of the 'Prague Spring' was signalled by the occupation of the Czechoslovakian capital by a Soviet airborne division airlifted by a force of 250 military transport aircraft. As the operation was unopposed they were able to land at Prague's Letnaný and Ruzyně airfields to unload troops and

LEFT: Soviet military activity in Cuba in 1962 alerted the free world to the extent of their territorial ambitions.

ABOVE: SA-3 missiles attract the attention of the Moscow crowd at a military parade.

equipment, rather than air-dropping them. The airborne troops swiftly secured the airfields and then occupied such strategic points in the city as the radio stations. As ground forces advanced into Czechoslovakia from East Germany, Hungary and Poland, they were covered by some 500 tactical aircraft drawn from the Soviet 24th Air Army in East Germany (later renumbered the 16th Air Army and now the Air Forces of the Group of Soviet Forces in Germany), the 37th Air Army in Poland and the Southern Group of Soviet Forces' Air Army in Hungary, together with units of these Warsaw Pact national air forces. In fact as opposition to the occupying forces was disorganized and minimal, there were no calls for air support. However, the entire operation was conducted under the cover of a barrage of ECM jamming provided by Frontal Aviation. Although preceded by a period of considerable tension, the Soviet occupation of Czechoslovakia apparently came as a surprise to the NATO forces. One of the most interesting lessons of the operation was the convincing demonstration by the Warsaw Pact forces of their ability to mount relatively large-scale troop and air movements with a minimum of advanced warning.

A more active role for Soviet air forces came with their involvement in Egypt's air defense in the aftermath of the Six Day War of 1967. The Soviet Union had reequipped the Egyptian forces with early model MiG-21s and SA-2 Guideline SAMs, but these were unable to prevent the Israeli Air

BELOW: A Tupolev Tu-20 Bear-D glides through the stratosphere under the power of four mighty Kuznetsov turboprops driving eight propellers mounted in counter-rotating pairs. RIGHT: A sister aircraft is intercepted by a Royal Air Force F-4 Phantom as it strays dangerously close to British airspace.

BELOW: Egyptian MiG-17s strafe an Israeli convoy near the Suez Canal, 1967.

INSET OPPOSITE: Three MiG-21s lie destroyed on their home airfield, victims of pre-emptive Israeli attack during the 1967 conflict.

Force flying virtually at will over Egyptian territory. By January 1970 the Egyptian government recognized that it was powerless to prevent Israeli bombing raids, which had penetrated deep into the Nile Delta and destroyed military targets on the outskirts of Cairo. Accordingly President Nasser appealed to the Soviet Union for more modern equipment. This was provided together with Soviet personnel to man it, as the Soviet High Command did not believe that the Egyptians had the necessary skill. They were also worried that new equipment might be captured intact by the Israelis, as had happened in December 1969 when a heliborne commando raid seized a Spoon Rest early-warning radar from the Egyptians.

Low altitude SAM coverage was provided by SA-3 Goa missiles, which were first deployed in the Nile Delta area and later moved forward to the Suez Canal. Fighter aircraft were provided both by Frontal Aviation and by the Air Defense Forces. Two regiments of MiG-21MF Fishbed-Js, which had more powerful engines and improved armament in comparison with the Egyptian Air Force's models, were withdrawn from the Soviet air army in Hungary and installed on Egyptian airfields. A third fighter regiment of Su-15 Flagons (some reports say Su-9/11 Fishpots) was provided by the Odessa Air Defense District and Soviet-manned radars and control centers coordinated the operations of

ground and air systems. The entire force was commanded by a general seconded from the Moscow Air Defense District.

By the end of March 1970 the Soviet air defense forces were in place and in April the Israeli Air Force curtailed its raids deep into Egypt in order to avoid a confrontation with Soviet forces. However, as the Soviet air defense commander began to push his SA-2 and SA-3 missile screen forward from the Nile towards the Suez Canal, the SAM sites came under attack from Israeli A-4 Skyhawks and F-4 Phantoms. The Israelis did not have ECM equipment and so suffered losses to the SA-3s. On 30 July 1970 Soviet MiG-21s intercepted a force of Israeli F-4

Phantoms and Mirage IIIs. During the ensuing battle five Soviet fighters were shot down in return for one Mirage damaged in combat. The highly-trained Israeli pilots were not impressed by their opponents' tactical skills, although they admitted that the Soviet pilots were outnumbered. A week later the United Nations ceasefire ended the combats over the Canal and so there was no further opportunity for the Israelis to test the mettle of the Soviet Air Force. The combat-hardened Israeli pilots would have been tough opponents for any air force and so it is probably wrong to assume that Soviet flying and tactical skills were seriously deficient at this time simply on the basis of one encounter. However, the skirmishes of 1970 indicated that the Soviet forces tended to rely on ground-based SAM and AA systems for tactical air defense, rather than fighter aircraft. The experience of the 1973 war, fought by the Egyptians with Soviet equipment and tactics after the withdrawal of Soviet personnel, provided further evidence that this was the preferred Soviet doctrine.

In addition to the air defense forces, the Soviet Air Force deployed various reconnaissance and ELINT aircraft to Egypt in 1970-72: the Naval Air Force operated in support of Soviet warships based at Alexandria and Military Transport Aviation maintained an air link between Cairo West air base and the Soviet Union. Four MiG-25R Foxbat-B reconnaissance aircraft flew missions over Israeli-occupied Sinai and the coast of Israel itself during the period from October 1971 to May 1972 and they remained in Egypt until October 1972 – the last Soviet aircraft to be withdrawn. Be-12 Mail and Il-38 May maritime reconnaissance aircraft patrolled the eastern Mediterranean from bases at Mersa Matruh and Jiyanklis and Tu-16 Badgers of the Naval Air Force operated from Aswan. Electronic intelligence was undertaken by a small number of An-12 Cub-B aircraft. The mainstay of the airlift was the Cub-A tactical transport, but a number of An-22 Cocks also operated into Egypt. By July 1972, when President Sadat ordered the Soviet forces out of the country, there were around 17,000 Soviet personnel in Egypt. Soviet involvement in the Yom Kippur War was restricted to the airlift of arms and ammunition to Egypt and Syria. This operation involved between 60 and 90 flights per day and an estimated 15,000,000 tons of supplies were delivered. It is instructive to compare this tonnage, lifted during 930 sorties, with the USAF resupply effort to Israel, which delivered over 22,000,000 tons in only 567 sorties, despite the greater distances involved.

In the mid 1970s Soviet transport aircraft were committed to the support of Communist MPLA forces during the civil war in Angola. This involved an airlift over a distance of some 6000 miles from Soviet air bases – in contrast to the flights to Egypt where the distance covered was some 1250 miles. Military Transport Aviation's new Il-76 Candids performed the greater part of these missions, backed up by heavy-lift An-22 Cocks and Aeroflot Il-62 Classics for trooping. Although Soviet forces were not directly involved in the fighting, Cuban troops and airmen did engage in combat. In order to release MiG-21 pilots from the Cuban Air Force for service in Angola, Frontal Aviation pilots were sent to Cuba. However, elsewhere in Africa and the Middle East the Soviet Union has become more directly involved with regional armed forces, both by supplying arms and by seconding trained personnel to

operate them. Since 1974 Libya has operated relatively advanced Soviet warplanes, largely through the assistance of Soviet pilots and maintenance crews as few Libyans possess the necessary technical skills. The former USAF base, Wheelus Field (now Okba Ben Nafi) is occupied by a regiment of MiG-25 Foxbat-A interceptors, a squadron of Foxbat-B/C reconnaissance aircraft, a regiment of Tu-22 Blinder bombers and a regiment of Su-20 Fitters (an export model of the Su-17). At the former RAF airfield at

OPPOSITE: Another East-meets-West confrontation between Bear and Phantom.
TOP: A MiG-21 interceptor fighter is readied for flight.
ABOVE: A Flogger unleashes an air-to-surface rocket attack.

El Adem there is a regiment of MiG-23 Floggers and helicopter units fly Mi-24 Hinds and Mi-8 Hips. It is thought that the MiG-25s are operated exclusively by Soviet pilots, although Libyan and other Arab aircrew are attached to the other units. Libyan Tu-22s have carried out bombing raids in support of guerrilla forces in Chad in 1980 and two Su-20s were lost in combat during a skirmish with F-14 Tomcats of the US Sixth Fleet in August 1981. Soviet crews may well have taken part in the raids on Chad, but the Su-20s were piloted by Arabs.

Soviet involvement in Ethiopia's successful Ogaden campaign against Somalia in 1978 was far greater and indeed the operation was commanded by a Soviet officer, General Vasily Petrov. The Air Force's contribution included a massive airlift of supplies and personnel from the Soviet Union to Addis Ababa, which at its peak involved over 200 transport aircraft. Cuban troops were airlifted into the combat theater, together with Soviet advisors and technical specialists. Armored vehicles, artillery and aircraft were despatched by sea and air. In

November and December 1977 Military Transport Aviation flew some 12,500 Cuban and Soviet personnel into Ethiopia. Soviet pilots operated alongside Cuban and Ethiopian personnel in the fighter units, which operated some 50 MiG-21s, 25 MiG-23s and a single squadron of United States-supplied F-5s. MiG-21 Fishbed-H tactical reconnaissance aircraft were operated over Somali territory by Soviet pilots on the eve of the offensive. In late January MiG-21s, operating as fighter-bombers, attacked the Somali forces' lines of supply.

Air opposition was slight, because most of Somalia's small air force (Soviet-supplied MiG-17s, MiG-21s and Il-28s) was grounded due to lack of spares. Consequently the Ethiopian air force could concentrate on ground attack and all land operations were well supported.

A small helicopter force of 20 Mi-8 Hip assault transports and ten heavy-lift Mi-6 Hooks made a major contribution to the campaign. The key position in the Somali defenses was the town of Jijiga, which dominated the only practicable pass through

BELOW: The death plunge of an Egyptian MiG-21, 1973. Combats between Arab MiGs and Israeli Phantoms and Mirages have rarely ended favorably for pilots of the Soviet interceptor.

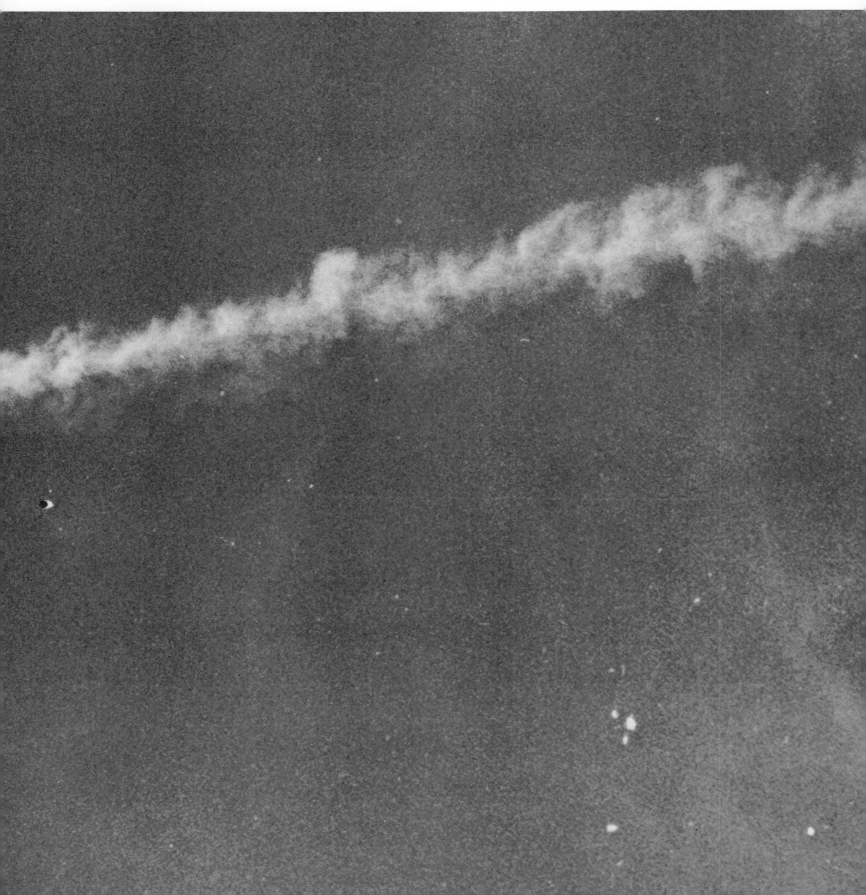

the Ahmar Mountains. Once these defenses were breached, the Ethiopian armored forces could readily deploy in the easy terrain of the Ogaden desert. The assault on Jijiga combined a heavy frontal attack with an armored thrust from the defenders' rear mounted by forces lifted over the mountain barrier by the helicopters. The Mi-6s lifted assault guns and APCs, while the Mi-8s carried troops and thereafter provided fire support. Airborne forces were dropped to secure landing zones and MiG-21s provided air cover and close air support for the raiding force. The operation proved to be a reenactment in actual warfare – albeit on a small scale – of the vertical envelopment maneuvers which the Soviet armed forces have so often practiced during exercises.

In contrast to the economical and swift Soviet victory in the Ogaden, the war in Afghanistan has proved to be both protracted and bloody. Between late December 1979 and the end of January 1980 the Soviet Army moved seven divisions of troops into the country. The force was spearheaded by the 105th Airborne Division, which was ferried into Kabul airport by some 280 Il-76 Candid, An-12 Cub and An-22 Cock transports. Small heliborne parties were used to occupy key positions. Air cover for all troop movements was provided by MiG-21 Fishbeds and MiG-23 Floggers operating from Karshi and Kerki airfields in the Soviet Union. By late January the Soviet Air Force was operating from a number of Afghan airfields, including Bagram, Kabul, Kandahar and Shindand. Each airfield was occupied by several squadrons of MiG-21 fighter-bombers and a small force of fixed-wing and helicopter transports. However it soon became apparent that helicopters were the most useful aircraft to support the Soviet Army's counter-insurgency operations in mountainous terrain, where fast-flying jet aircraft were unable to locate and attack fleeting targets with sufficient precision. Consequently it was the helicopter force that was built up in Afghanistan during the 1980s to a strength of around 500 aircraft.

LEFT: Soviet interceptors sweep across the sky under the direction of a ground radar station.

RIGHT: A Hind observer's view of Western Europe. The powerfully-armed gunship would prove as potent a force in any conflict there as it has already proved in Afghanistan.

Armed helicopters are used to provide close air support for ground forces, to transport infantry on search and destroy operations and to escort road convoys. Mi-8 Hip transport helicopters carry out cordon operations by landing infantry in positions around a suspected rebel stronghold which, once surrounded, can be systematically reduced. The problem as in all guerrilla conflicts is in pinning down an elusive enemy. Often special air assault brigades are used for this role and as many as five may be committed in Afghanistan. Road convoys are escorted by armed Mi-8 Hip-E helicopters or Mi-24 Hinds. They generally carry an infantry squad which can be landed on commanding heights along the route. Helicopters have also proved useful in pulling out troops from untenable positions. Yet it is the Mi-24 Hind attack helicopters which have proved to be the key weapon in the war against the Afghan guerrillas. This helicopter's armored protection has generally proved to be impervious to small arms fire, although a number of Hinds have been brought down by plunging fire through their unprotected top surfaces when guerrillas have been able to fire down on them from commanding ridges. When operating against fortified guerrilla positions, the Hind's rocket armament has proved to be especially useful. Generally the attack helicopters fly in mutually-supporting pairs – the classic *zveno* formation – sometimes directed by a higher-flying scout helicopter. During operations in conjunction with ground forces, the Hinds act as flying artillery and carry out armed reconnaissance sweeps in advance of the troops. They share the task of precision air strikes with a small force of fixed-wing aircraft,

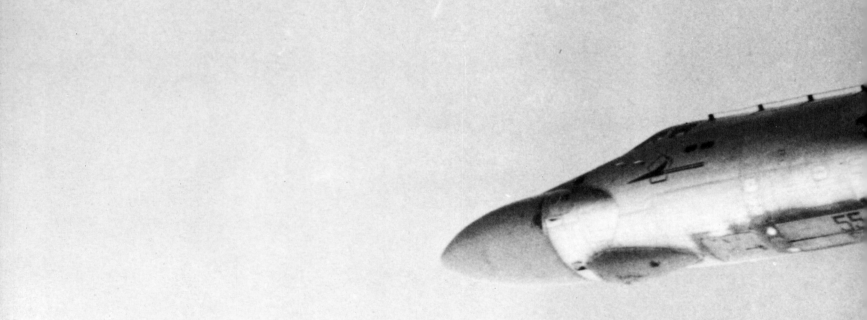

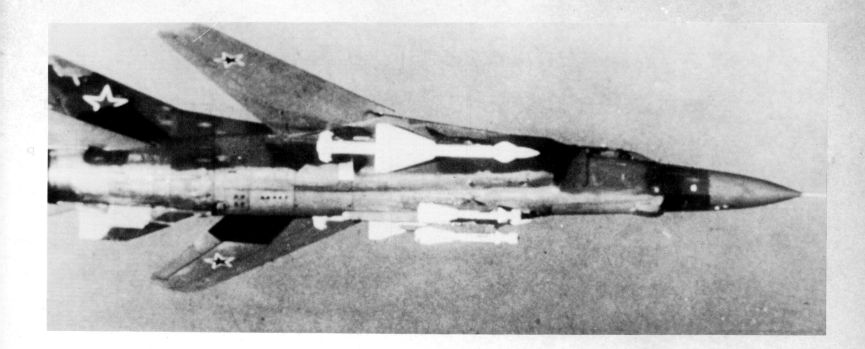

Su-25 Frogfoots and MiG-21s. The Su-25 is a maneuverable aircraft with good endurance and a large weapons load, and is thus well suited to conditions in Afghanistan.

In general the military involvement in Afghanistan has given Soviet officers and men a valuable experience in the hard school of combat. However, this has proved more useful to Army personnel than to the Air Force's pilots – with the notable exception of the helicopter crews. Afghanistan certainly cannot be compared with the bitterly fought air war over North Vietnam which had such a profound effect on the combat training of American military pilots. Soviet pilots have seen very little action since World War II. However, there is every reason to suppose that they have followed recent air campaigns abroad with interest and most probably profited from their lessons.

In June 1982 Israeli Air Force fighters (including F-15 Eagles and F-16 Fighting Falcons) engaged Syrian MiG-23 Floggers and MiG-21 Fishbeds over the Bekaa Valley. Assisted by an E-2C Hawkeye airborne early warning aircraft, the Israelis com-

pletely outfought the Syrians and claimed 22 victories in one combat and 25 in a second. During the same operations they knocked out Syrian SA-6 sites on the ground. According to one senior Israeli officer, the Syrian losses were due to inept tactics rather than any shortcomings in the MiG-23's design. However, the officer did criticize the MiG-25 Foxbat-A interceptor, which had also been met in combat, for its poor performance and maneuverability at low altitude and the limited visibility from the cockpit. He was also highly critical of the efficiency of the Syrians' Soviet SA-2s, SA-3s and SA-6s, blaming their poor performance on limitations of the missiles themselves rather than on Syrian mistakes in operating them. In the Israeli view the Soviet doctrine of substituting ground-based defenses for fighter air cover is not effective. Presumably Soviet advisors in Syria have reported on the tactical lessons of these engagements and they can hardly have presented them as anything but serious defeats. Even when due allowance is made for the Israelis' high level of tactical skill and Syrian deficiencies in this respect, the

BELOW: An artist's impression of the Tu-26 Backfire at altitude.

RIGHT: Antonov's Condor will be the largest aircraft in the world when it enters service. Its maximum payload is likely to be an impressive 264,000lb.

BELOW RIGHT: The Su-15 Flagon interceptor will gradually be phased out as MiG-23s leave the production lines in greater numbers.

LEFT: Backfire with its variable-geometry wing swept forward. The nose refueling probes have since been removed from operational aircraft as a gesture to prove to the US that the Tu-26 is a tactical – not a strategic – bomber.

technological gap between Western and Soviet equipment must worry Soviet commanders.

Doubts also remain about the level of tactical and flying skills of Soviet pilots, although there is evidence that in recent years the Soviet Air Force has improved the realism of its combat training. Furthermore, there are signs that at last a measure of individual initiative on the part of the fighter pilot is being encouraged. However, in this respect the Soviet forces face the dilemma that any undue emphasis on initiative at junior levels will undermine the traditions of discipline and strict subordination which commanders see as one of the great strengths of the Soviet military system. Assuming that the Soviet Air Force's improved tactical training programs can produce pilots of equal skill to those of the Western air forces and that the new generation of Soviet fighter aircraft will have much the same agility as the F-15 or F-16, then by the late 1980s Soviet fighter regiments will be performing the air superiority mission very effectively.

The morale of the Soviet pilot – and of the maintenance, supply and administrative personnel who support him – will have a crucial effect on the performance of the Soviet Air Force in action. Highly colored journalistic accounts in the West have portrayed the Soviet serviceman as discontented, habitually drunken and generally inefficient. This picture is a caricature, but nonetheless is not wholly inaccurate. The life of a Soviet conscript is undoubtedly hard; he is poorly paid, has little opportunity for off-duty recreation and is constantly subjected to a harsh – and sometimes brutal – discipline. The position of a junior officer is certainly more privileged, but his life too is bounded by the inflexible military code. Under such conditions it would be surprising if the Soviet serviceman did not seek relief in off-duty drunken sprees. His counterpart in the West has been known to do the same. Most accounts of Soviet military life are concerned specifically with the Army, but Lieutenant Viktor Belenko, the MiG-25 pilot who defected with his fighter to Japan in 1976, has drawn an equally harsh picture of conditions in the Air Defense Forces. The problem with the testimony of defectors is that they must show the Soviet services in the worst possible

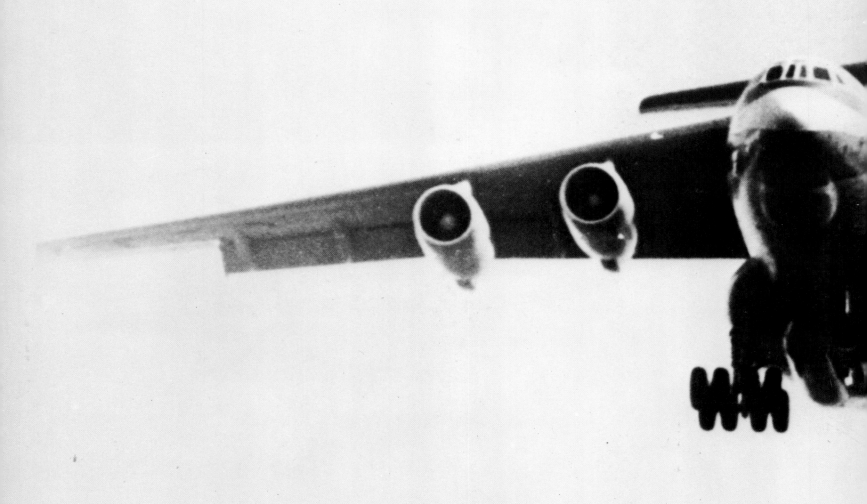

light in order to justify their action in deserting. No doubt their evidence is factually correct, but it does not reflect the attitudes of the great majority of Soviet servicemen who are prepared to put up with military life. This argument can be taken a stage further to suggest that the Soviet system may well produce tough and resilient servicemen well adapted to withstanding the rigors of warfare.

The past decade has been a period of far-reaching change for the Soviet air forces, during which they have expanded both their combat capabilities and areas of operation to a significant degree. Not only have they built two tactical combat aircraft for every one produced in the United States during this period, but they have also steadily improved the technical quality of their designs. The Soviet air forces are therefore approaching the time when their warplanes can match Western combat aircraft in terms of individual capability, while greatly outnumbering them. The new generation of Soviet aircraft, such as the MiG-31 Foxhound interceptor, the Su-27 Flanker and MiG-29 Fulcrum fighters, the Mainstay airborne warning and control aircraft, the Blackjack strategic bomber and Condor strategic transport, will be well established in service by the end of the present decade. They are equivalent in general capability to the United States aircraft of the early 1970s, most of which will not be fully replaced until the 1990s. Therefore a gap in technological capability certainly remains, but it is closing perceptibly. It is at present too early to forecast the quantities in which the new warplanes will enter service. The production of military aircraft in the Soviet Union has dropped from an annual rate of 1200 in the late 1970s to about 1000 in 1983. The reduction may simply be a short-term result of the unavoidable disruption caused by switching production to new and more complex designs. Alternatively it may be that even the large Soviet defense budget cannot afford to finance advanced technology aircraft in the same numbers as the robust and relatively simple warplanes of the previous generation. Should the yearly production figures again creep up to the 1200 mark, then Soviet air power will indeed rest on a formidable combination of quality and quantity.

BELOW: The wide body, STOL wing and high-flotation landing gear of the Il-76 are all evident in this view of the Soviets' biggest operational jet transport to date.

INDEX

Page numbers in italics refer to illustrations

Aeroflot 35, 45, 71, 115, 121, 123
Afghanistan 39, 30-1, 55, 95, 102, 110, 113, 114, 183-4, 186
Air Defense Forces 8, 27, 28, 29, 36, 42, 44, 70-87, 92, 97-8, 133, 164, 169, 170, 176
  command structure 70-1
  operational doctrine 74-5, 169
Air Force Schools and Academies 29, 39, 133, 136
air superiority role 15, 91, 92, 94, 98, 169, 188
airborne command posts 65-6, 67, 111, 113, 126
airborne forces 11-12, 21, 27, 28, 42, 42, 44, 91, 102, 121-3, 125
airborne warning and control aircraft 73, 74, 126
aircraft, British
  Lightning 20, 91
  Sea Harrier 155
aircraft, French
  Breguet-Dornier Alpha Jet 111
  Mirage III 156, 179
aircraft, Polish
  TS-11 Iskra 137
aircraft, Romanian
  IAR 93 137
aircraft, Soviet
  see also helicopters, Soviet
  Aero L-29 Delfin 137
  Aero L-39 Albatros 135, 137
  An-2 Colt 125, 129, 130, 133, 137
  An-10 civil airliner 123
  An-12 Cub 35, 37, 65-6, 117, 121, 122-3, 123, 125, 126, 129, 149, 183
    Cub-A 126, 179
    Cub-B 126, 161, 179
    Cub-C 97, 126
  An-22 Cock 35, 37, 120, 123, 124, 125, 126, 127-8, 129, 136, 179, 183
  An-24 129, 133
  An-26 Curl 125, 129, 132-3
  An-30 129, 131
  An-32 128, 129
  An-40, An-400 Condor 128, 187, 189
  An-72 Coaler 127, 129, 129-30
  Be-12 Mail 144, 149, 155, 157, 179
  Blackjack 46-7, 57, 61, 62, 189
  Il-2 Shturmovik 39, 95, 114, 164, 167, 169
  Il-10 167
  Il-14 Crate 125, 130, 133
  Il-18 Coot 86, 125, 130, 134, 149
    Coot-A 161
  Il-28 167, 181
  Il-38 May 149, 156, 156-7, 179

Il-62 Classic 120, 125, 133, 134, 179
Il-76 Candid 4, 15, 35, 37, 65, 66, 73, 74, 118-19, 120, 121, 123-6, 124, 129, 179, 183, 189
Il-76 Mainstay 73, 74, 78, 126, 189
Il-86 66, 67, 125
MiG-15 137, 167, 168, 169-70
MiG-17 32, 137, 167, 171, 176, 181
MiG-19 32, 35, 167, 171, 171
MiG-21 Fishbed 15, 22, 23, 30, 70-1, 71, 77, 91, 93, 94, 97, 98, 167, 168, 171, 173, 177, 177, 179, 179, 181, 181, 183, 186
  Fishbed-C 15, 39, 94
  Fishbed-H 96, 97, 181
  Fishbed-J 176
  Fishbed-L 14, 31, 72
  Fishbed-N 15, 94
MiG-21U 135, 137
MiG-23 Flogger 6-7, 22, 41, 43, 71, 74, 76, 78, 92, 93, 97, 98, 140, 166, 179, 180, 181, 183, 186
  Flogger-B 77, 91, 93, 94, 184
  Flogger-F 90, 94
  Flogger-G 2-3, 75, 77, 93
MiG-23U 137
Mig-25 Foxbat 22, 74, 76, 77, 77, 78, 93, 96, 98, 166, 180
  Foxbat-A 76, 179, 186
  Foxbat-B 65, 96-7, 97, 179
  Foxbat-C 179
  Foxbat-D 65, 96-7, 97
  Foxbat-E 75, 76, 167
MiG-25M Foxhound 76; *see* MiG-31
MiG-25U 137
MiG-27 Flogger 41, 77, 90, 92, 93-5, 96, 97, 98, 140, 161
  Flogger-D 91, 94
  Flogger-J 94
MiG-29 Fulcrum 75, 78, 78, 94, 98, 189
MiG-31 Foxhound-A 75, 76, 78, 189
Mya-4 Bison 33, 34, 56, 56, 57, 58, 60, 61, 164
  Bison-B 60, 65
Ram-M (USDIA designation) 65
Su-7 Fitter 71, 94, 98
  Fitter-A 94, 95
  Fitter-B 94
Su-9 75, 77, 78, 97, 176
Su-11 Fishpot 75, 77, 78, 176
Su-15 Flagon 19, 71, 71, 77-8, 176, 187
Su-17 Fitter 41, 41, 90, 91, 92, 94-5, 96, 97, 98, 140, 144, 149, 161, 179
  Fitter-C 13, 94
  Fitter-D 88-9, 94
  Fitter-H 94, 96, 97
Su-20 (Su-17) 179, 180
Su-21 Flagon-F 77
Su-22 162-3

Su-24 Fencer 21, 34, 34, 38, 56, 60, 62, 63, 66-7, 91, 93, 95, 161, 185
Su-25 Frogfoot 31, 92, 95, 98, 111, 186
Su-27 Flanker 75, 78, 78, 94, 140, 189
TB-3 111
Tu-16 Badger 24-5, 34, 56, 57, 59, 60, 62, 63-5, 64, 67, 144, 149, 161, 164, 179, 184
  Badger-C 158
  Badger-D 65, 65, 161
  Badger-E, F, K 65, 161
  Badger-G 158
  Badger-H 64-5, 161
  Badger-J 64-5, 161
Tu-16 Chinese-built 32
Tu-20 Bear 34, 56, 57, 57-8, 60, 61, 66, 149, 164, 178
  Bear-D 20, 32, 34, 161, 175
  Bear-E 60-, 65
  Bear-F 149, 156
Tu-22 Blinder 56, 60, 61, 63-4, 67, 149, 158, 179, 180
  Blinder-B 61
  Blinder-C 60, 60, 65, 161
Tu-22U 137
Tu-26 Backfire 21, 32, 34, 56, 57, 58, 60, 61-2, 67, 144, 149, 157, 157, 158, 161, 186
Tu-28P Fiddler 74, 75, 75, 78
Tu-114 airliner 74
Tu-126 Moss 73, 73, 74, 78
Tu-134 Crusty 125, 133
Tu-154 Careless 125, 133
Yak-18 136, 137
Yak-25RD Mandrake 65
Yak-28 Brewer 34, 67, 98, 167
  Brewer-D 96, 97
  Brewer-E 97
Yak-28P Firebar 75, 78, 78
Yak-28U 35
Yak-36 Forger 38, 45, 140, 140-1, 144, 145, 148, 149, 151, 155-6, 158, 161
Yak-40 Codling 125, 133, 134
Yak-52 136
aircraft, United States
  A3D Skywarrior 140
  A-4 Skyhawk 177
  A-6, A-7 142
  A-10 Thunderbolt II 95, 99
  AJ Savage 140
  B-1 61, 73
  B-52 61, 73
  B-70 Valkyrie 76
  C-5A Galaxy 127, 128
  C-130 Hercules 117, 126
    MC-130E 123
    TACAMO Hercules 66
  RC-135 71
  C-141 Starlifter 124
  E-2C Hawkeye 186
  E-3 Sentry 71, 74
  E-3A AWACS 58
  F-4 Phantom 22, 56, 62, 91, 92, 175, 177, 178, 179
  F-5 181
  F-14 Tomcat 156, 180
  F-15 Eagle 58, 90, 93, 96, 186, 188
  F-16 Fighting Falcon 90, 93, 94, 186, 188
  F-18 Hornet 94
  F-86 Sabre 169-70

F-104 Starfighter 91
F-106 58
F-111 66, 67
SP-2H Neptune 138-9
P-3 Orion 122, 156
TR-1A 71
U-2 65, 80, 164
Advanced Technology bomber 73-4
aircraft, West German
  Breguet-Dornier Alpha Jet 111
aircraft carriers 45, 140, 142, 157-8, 161
Akhromeyev, Marshal Sergei 26, 26, 27
amphibious warfare 161
Andropov, Yuri 9, 27
Angola civil war 120-1, 179
anti-air operations 42, 44, 90, 91
anti-ballistic missile systems 49, 50, 70, 73, 79, 81, 83, 86, 87
  ABM-1 Galosh 52, 73
  SH-4, SH-8 73
anti-satellite weapons 14, 85, 86, 87
anti-shipping strikes 151, 155
anti-submarine warfare 42, 45, 140-41, 144, 146-7, 149, 151, 154, 156-7
Arab-Israeli conflicts 173, 176, 179, 186
  see also Six Day War, Yom Kippur War
artillery
  Anti-aircraft 72, 79, 91, 97-9, 179
  ZSU-23-4 cannon 81, 98, 99, 117
  artillery support 2, 44, 91
Aviation Armies of the Soviet Union 29, 34, 39, 42, 56, 60, 62-3, 66-7, 133, 157

Ballistic missile warning systems 70
Batekhin, Colonel-General L L 39
battlefield surveillance drone 96
Belenko, Lieutenant Viktor 188
Belov, Major General M 112
bomber aircraft 34-5, 42, 56, 70
  attack and light bombers 38
  cruise missile armed 51, 57, 60
  long range 34, 56-8, 60-3, 67
  medium range 34, 56, 57, 60-5, 67
Brezhnev, Leonid 27, 48
Bugnayev, Marshal P B 123

Carrier battle groups 45, 140, 157-8, 161
chemical weapons 42, 44, 67, 91, 95-6
Chernenko, Konstantin 27
China, People's Republic of 31, 78
  air force 31-2, 60
  ballistic missiles in 32
  targets in 60, 62
Churilov, Lieutenant Colonel 39
Clausewitz, Carl von 8
close air support 38, 41, 44, 105, 114, 169, 184
command and control systems 17, 18, 20

Communist Party 8, 27, 28, 137
conscripts 8-9, 18, 22, 23, 188
Cuba
  Soviet aircraft in 23, 149, 156
  Soviet missiles in 48
  Soviet personnel in 179
  use of Cuban forces 9, 121,
    179, 180-1
Czechoslovakia, occupation of
  121, 122, 173

Defense Council 26-7
directed-energy beam weapons
  26-7

Egorov, Admiral G M 18
Egyptian air force 22, 64, 79, 94,
  173, 176, 179
electronic counter-measures
  (ECCM) 17
electronic countermeasures
  (ECM) 17, 60, 63, 65,
  90, 97 98
electronic intelligence (ELINT)
  20, 60, 65, 71, 86, 161,
  179
electronic support measures
  (ESM) 74
electronic warfare aircraft role
  64, 90, 97, 144, 155, 161
Ethiopian War 102, 117, 121,
  180-1, 183
exercises, Soviet military 107,
  111, 114, 123

Falkland Islands campaign 156
fighter aircraft 38, 45, 71
  air superiority 38, 44, 74, 78,
    90, 91, 92, 94
  ground attack 38, 74, 78, 90,
    91, 95, 98
  tactical 41, 70, 71
flexible response strategy 9
flying training 133, 136-7
Frontal Aviation 10, 15, 16, 23,
  29, 34, 38, 39, 44, 56,
  65, 67, 70, 74, 76, 77,
  78, 90-9, 102, 129, 133,
  145, 161, 167, 173, 176,
  179
  aircraft strength, table 98
  helicopter strength, table 107
  organization 90, 91-2, 103
  target selection 90-91, 96

Gorbachev, Mikhail 26, 27
Gorshkov, Admiral Sergei 10,
  39, 42, 140, 144, 151
Great Patriotic War 9, 10-11,
  20, 26, 27, 33, 39, 97,
  164, 167, 169
Grechko, Marshal A A 26, 27
ground attack aircraft 15, 38, 91,
  94, 95, 167
ground support operations 10,
  33, 42, 96

Heliborne troops 21, 44, 91,
  104-5, 107, 108, 183
helicopter assault troops 42, 102,
  104-5
helicopters 29, 34, 44, 90, 102-
  5, 107-17
  anti-helicopter helicopter 112

regimental organization 103-4
Ka-25 Hormone 40, 142-3,
  144, 145, 149, 151, 151,
  152-3, 154, 161
  Hormone-A 151
  Hormone-B, C 154
Ka-27 Helix 144, 149, 149,
  150, 154, 161
  Helix-A 154
  Helix-B 155
Ka-32 helix 149
Mi-1 Hare 103, 105, 106, 107,
  113, 117
Mi-2 Hoplite 103, 107, 113,
  115, 117
Mi-4 Hound 16, 103, 107,
  107, 111, 117
Mi-6 Hook 102-3, 103, 104,
  106, 107, 111, 112-13,
  117, 181, 183
Mi-8 Hip 9, 17, 18, 45, 66,
  103, 104, 107, 107, 110-
  11, 112, 114-15, 114-16,
  149, 157, 180, 181, 183,
  184
  Hip-C 116
  Hip-E 116, 161, 184
  Hip-J, K 113
Mi-14 Haze 116, 144, 149,
  154, 157, 158
  Haze-A, B 157
Mi-17 Hip-H 116
Mi-24 Hind 44, 103, 14, 107,
  110-11, 112, 112, 113-
  14, 169, 180, 184
  Hind-A 44, 114
  Hind-D 90, 104, 104, 107,
    110, 114, 117
  Hind-E 104, 107, 110, 114,
    117
  Hind-F 100-1, 114
Mi-26 Halo 103, 104, 107,
  108-9, 110, 111, 113,
  117, 117
Mi-28 Havoc 112
hovercraft 160-1, 161

Indian air force 94
in-flight refueling 24-5, 57, 58,
  63, 64, 65, 74, 144, 156,
  161
interceptor aircraft 36, 70-1, 72,
  74, 75-8, 92, 94
interdiction role 21, 34, 38, 41,
  42, 44, 56, 60, 61, 67,
  90, 91, 94, 96
Iran 30-1
Ivan Rogov, amphibious landing
  ship 161

Japan 31, 32
Jaruzelski, General 28
jet engines, introduction of 164,
  169

Kanin class destroyers 151
Kara, guided missile cruiser 150
  class 151
Kashin class destroyers 151
Kharkov, carrier 145
Khripin, General Vasili 11
Khrushchev, Nikita 26, 27, 48
Kiev, carrier 38, 144-5, 148, 158,
  161
  class 36, 45, 140, 143, 145,
  149, 151, 154, 155

Kirov, battlecruiser 151
Koldunov, Marshal A I 70
Korea, conflict in 169-70
Korean Air Lines incident 18,
  70, 71
Kotlin class destroyers 151
Kozhedub, Ivan 39
Kresta class cruisers 151, 159
Kulikov, Marshal Victor G 28,
  28
Kutakhov, Marshal Pavel S 10,
  27, 36, 38-9, 169
Kynda-class cruisers 151

Lenin, V I 8
Libya, Soviet aircraft in 179-80
Long Range Aviation 11, 34, 56,
  164

Massive retaliation strategy 9
Meskvitelev, Colonel-General I
  75
Mil, Mikhail 115
mine countermeasures 157
Military Transport Aviation 29,
  35, 39, 42, 120-30, 133,
  136-7, 179, 181
  aircraft strength, table 125
Minsk, carrier 38, 145, 146, 148,
  150
Mironenko, Colonel-General A
  A 39, 144
missiles, air-to-air 91
  AA-2 Atoll 93, 94
  AA-2-2 Advanced Atoll 93,
    94
  AA-3 Anab 77, 78
  AA-5 Ash 78
  AA-6 Acrid 76, 77
  AA-7 Apex 77, 93
  AA-8 Aphid 76, 77, 93, 94,
    112, 155
  AA-9 76, 94
missiles, air-to-surface 57, 58,
  95, 179
  AS-3 Kangaroo 60
  AS-4 Kitchen 58, 60, 62, 63,
    157, 158
  AS-5 Kelt 64, 158
  AS-6 Kingfish 62, 64, 158
  AS-7 Kerry 67, 95, 155
  AS-9 95
  AS-10 95
  AS-X-14 95
missiles, anti-ship 45, 62, 157
  SS-N-3 Shaddock 154, 161
  SS-N-12 Sandbox 154, 161
missiles, anti-submarine
  SS-N-14 154
missiles, anti-tank
  AT-2 Swatter 114, 116
  AT-6 Spiral 114
missiles, cruise, Soviet
  AS-X-15 57, 61
  Kennel 59
missiles, cruise, United States
  70, 73, 76
missiles intercontinental
  ballistic (ICBM) 11, 51,
  167
  cold launch system for 14, 50,
    53
missiles, ICBM, Soviet
  SS-6 Sapwood 48, 84, 167
  SS-7 Saddler 48
  SS-9 Scarp 48-9, 53, 84
  SS-10 48

SS-11 Sego 48, 48, 49, 51
SS-13 Savage 48, 49, 51, 51
SS-17 (RS-16) 48, 50, 51, 53,
  55
SS-18 (RS-20) 48, 50, 51, 53-
  4, 55
SS-19 (RS-18) 48, 50, 51, 53,
  55
SS-X-24 54, 55
SS-X-25 54, 54, 55, 71
missiles, ICBM, United States
  Minuteman 49, 50
  MX system 50, 54
  Titan II 51
missiles, intermediate range
  (IRBM), Soviet
  SS-5 Skean 49, 55, 56, 84
  SS-4 Sandal 48, 55, 56, 84
  SS-20 51, 54, 55, 55-6, 128
missiles, IRBM, United States
  Pershing II 71, 81, 90
missiles, submarine-launched
  (SLBM), Soviet
  SS-N-4 Sark 48
  SS-N-6 52
  SS-N-8 141
  SS-N-18 141
missiles, SLBM, United States
  51, 140, 146
  Polaris 140, 146
  Poseidon 140, 156
  Trident 140, 146, 156
  Trident II 147
missiles, surface-to-air 70, 71,
  72, 79-81, 91, 97-9, 179
  SA-1 Guild 79, 79
  SA-2 Guideline 71, 79-80,
    98, 98, 170-1, 170-1,
    173, 177, 186
  SA-3 Goa 71, 80, 80, 81, 98,
    99, 173, 176, 177, 186
  SA-4 Ganef 71, 83, 99, 124,
    127
  SA-5 Gammon 71, 80, 81
  SA-6 Gainful 80, 80, 99, 99,
    186
  SA-7 Grail 98, 98, 99, 112
  SA-8 Gecko 80, 80, 98-9
  SA-9 Gaskin 83, 98, 99
  SA-10 79, 81
  SA-11 99
  SA-12 81, 81
  SA-13 98, 99
Moskva, helicopter carrier 138-
  9, 151
  class 143, 145, 145, 151, 154
multiple independently targeted
  re-entry vehicle (MIRV)
  49, 50, 51, 53, 54
mutually assured destruction
  concept 49

Nasser, Gamel Abdul 176
Naval Air Force 35-6, 39, 42, 45,
  62, 66, 120, 133, 140-2,
  144-7, 149, 151, 154-8,
  161, 179
  aircraft strength 142, 144-5,
    149
  organization 35-6, 144-5
  primary roles 142, 146, 151,
    157
NORAD air defense system 60,
  61
North Atlantic Treaty
  Organization (NATO) 9
  air forces 23, 30, 91
  defense strategy 9, 21, 30, 95